# Contents

G000292431

The Photocopy Masters are of three levels of difficulty,
● basic work
●● for all children
●●● enrichment and extension.

Numbers	●	●●	●●●
N1 Place-value	1	2	3
N2 Place-value		4	5
N3 Multiplication/division	6	7, 8	9
N4 Multiplication/division		10	
N5 Multiplication/division	11	12, 13	
N6 Multiplication/division		14	
N7 Fractions/decimals		15	
N8 Fractions/decimals		16, 17, 18	
N9 Fractions/decimals		19	20
N10 Addition/subtraction		21, 22	23
N11 Addition/subtraction		24	
N12 Addition/subtraction		25	
N13 Properties of number	26	27	28
N14 Properties of number		29	30
N15 Place-value	31	32, 33	
N16 Place-value		34	
N17 Multiplication/division		35, 36, 37	
N18 Multiplication/division		38, 39	40
N19 Multiplication/division		41	
N20 Multiplication/division		42, 43	
N21 Fractions/decimals		44	
N22 Fractions/decimals		45, 46, 47	
N23 Addition/subtraction		48, 49	
N24 Addition/subtraction	50	51, 52	
N25 Addition/subtraction	53	54, 55	
N26 Addition/subtraction		56, 57, 58	
N27 Properties of number		59, 60	
N28 Properties of number	61		62, 63
N29 Place-value		64, 65	
N30 Place-value	66		
N31 Multiplication/division		67	68
N32 Multiplication/division		69	
N33 Multiplication/division		70, 71	72
N34 Multiplication/division		73, 74	
N35 Percentages	75	76, 77	
N36 Fractions/decimals		78, 79, 80	
N37 Ratio/proportion		81, 82	

Numbers (cont.)	●	●●	●●●
N38 Ratio/proportion		83	84
N39 Addition/subtraction		85	
N40 Addition/subtraction		86	
N41 Properties of number	87	88	89
N42 Properties of number		90	91
N43 Properties of number		92	

Shape, Data and Measures	●	●●	●●●
M1 Length		93, 94	
M2 Weight		95	
M3 Capacity		96	
M4 Area		97, 98	
M5 Area		99	100
M6 Perimeter		101	
S1 Angle		102	
S2 Angle		103	104
S3 Coordinates		105	
S4 Reflection		106	107
S5 Rotation/translation		108	
S6 3-d shape		109	110
S7 2-d shape		111	
S8 2-d shape		112, 113	
S9 2-d shape			114
D1 Grouped data		115	116
D2 Pie charts		117	118
D3 Conversion graphs		119	
D4 Averages	120	121	
D5 Probability		122, 123	

Mixed problems	●	●●	●●●
Solving problems (1)		124	
Solving problems (2)		125	
Solving problems (3)		126	
Solving problems (4)		127	

Name _____

Rounding decimals

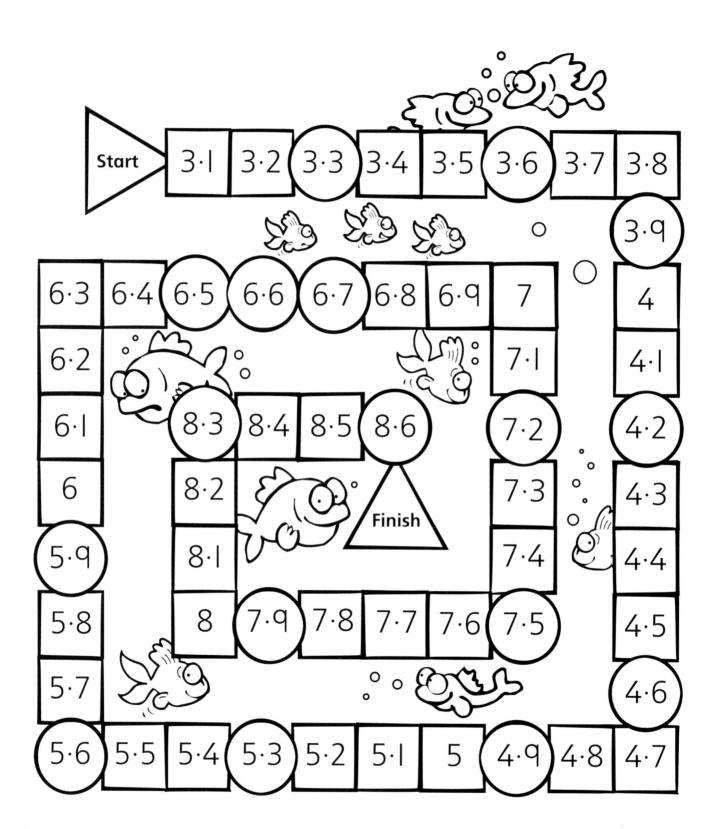

Teacher's instructions

A game for two players. Each place a counter at 'Start'. Take turns to throw the dice, and move your counter a matching number of spaces. If you land on a circle, move back or forward to the nearest whole number. The winner is the first to pass 'Finish'.

Materials
A dice
A counter each

1

Rounding to the nearest thousand

Round   **Score**

1

2

3

4

5

6

Total score

Teacher's instructions

A game for two players, each with a copy of this scoresheet.

Play round 1.

The dice is rolled, and both players write the number in one of their boxes.

After four rolls of the dice, each player has a 4-digit number.

They round this to the nearest thousand.

Score points to match the number of thousands, e.g. | 4 | 1 | 3 | 6 | → | 4 | 0 | 0 | 0 | 4 |

The winner is the player with the highest total score after six rounds.

Materials
A dice

2

Name _____

Nearest whole number

Choose three of the digits at the top of each column to make the nearest numbers.

Each digit can only be used once in a number.

Nearest whole number	③ ② ⑤ ⑧	④ ① ⑥ ⑦	② ⓪ ⑨ ④	③ ⑥ ④ ⑦
1	2·35	1·46	0·94	3·46
2				
3				
4				
5				
6				
7				
8				
9				
10				

3

Name _____

Dividing by 10 and 100

Divide each amount by 10.

1.

£38

£3·80

2.

£72

3.

£60

4.

£95

5.

£4

6.

£53

Divide each amount by 100.

7.

£421

8.

£360

9.

£725

10.

£582

11.

£109

12.

£470

Dividing by 10 and 100

Complete these.

1. $46 \div$ (____) $= 4.6$

2. $28 \div$ (____) $= 2.8$

3. (____) $\div 10 = 7.3$

4. (____) $\div 10 = 0.6$

5. (____) $\div 10 = 1.5$

6. $55 \div$ (____) $= 5.5$

7. (____) $\div 100 = 2.36$

8. (____) $\div 100 = 4.78$

9. $504 \div$ (____) $= 5.04$

10. (____) $\div 100 = 7.32$

11. $62 \div$ (____) $= 0.62$

12. (____) $\div 100 = 0.58$

13. (____) $\div 100 = 0.07$

14. (____) $\div 100 = 0.11$

15. $1.4 \div$ (____) $= 0.14$

16. $2 \div$ (____) $= 0.02$

17. (____) $\div 10 = 3.7$

18. (____) $\div 100 = 1.58$

19. $42 \div$ (____) $= 0.42$

20. (____) $\div 10 = 6.31$

Name _____

Division facts

Complete these.

1. $30 \div 6 =$ _____

2. $32 \div 4 =$ _____

3. $48 \div 6 =$ _____

4. $54 \div 6 =$ _____

5. $45 \div 5 =$ _____

6. $56 \div 8 =$ _____

7. $21 \div 7 =$ _____

8. $27 \div 9 =$ _____

9. $24 \div 3 =$ _____

10. $35 \div 5 =$ _____

11. $49 \div 7 =$ _____

12. $40 \div 8 =$ _____

13. $72 \div 9 =$ _____

14. $16 \div 4 =$ _____

15. $63 \div 7 =$ _____

16. $64 \div 8 =$ _____

17. $36 \div 4 =$ _____

18. $81 \div 9 =$ _____

19. $42 \div 7 =$ _____

20. $63 \div 9 =$ _____

Name _____

Division game

Board 1

6	8	1
2	4	q
5	7	3

Board 2

6	q	2
1	5	7
8	4	3

Teacher's instructions

A game for two players. Choose a board each. Take turns to throw both dice, and arrange them to show a 2-digit number:

24

7 Place a counter on any one of your board numbers that divides into your 2-digit number. The winner is the first to have a straight line of three counters.

Materials
2 dice
A set of counters each

Name _____

Multiplication facts

Complete these multiplication grids.

1.

×	2	3	4	5
2				
3				
4				
5				

2.

×	4	5	6	7
4				
5				
6				
7				

3.

×	7	8	9	2
3				
4				
5				
6				

4.

×	2	3	4	5
6				
7				
8				
9				

5.

×	5	3	6	4
7				
2				
8				
9				

6.

×	3	1	4	7
6				
0				
8				
5				

7.

×	3		6	5
2				
		32	48	
6				
9				

8.

×	2		8	7
5				
7		28		
		36		
		12		

9.

×	6	2		9
		56		
3		21		
		35		
4				

Name _____

Card multiplications

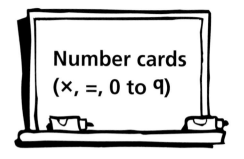

0 1 2 3 4 5 6 7 8 9

Make different multiplication facts with the cards.

Here are three.

$7 \times 4 = 28$

$5 \times 6 = 30$

$12 \times 5 = 60$

Investigate how many more you can make.

Investigate using 5 cards, 6 cards, and so on.

9

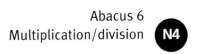

Name _____

Halving and doubling

Complete the grids.

2·6	7·6	5·9
6·4	3·4	4·7
8·3	1·9	7·2

doubled

3400	290	7600
470	4600	630
3800	390	8200

halved

9·6		13·4
	12·5	
3·9		7·8

doubled

	26·8	
15·6		31·4
	9·2	

10

Name _____

Multiplication tables

Complete these tables.

1.

×	4	6	5	7	3
10					
30					
50					
40					
20					

2.

×	50	90	60	80	70
2					
5					
4					
6					
3					

3.

×	3	5	7	4	6
200					
500					
300					
100					
400					

4.

×	600	800	500	700	900
2					
5					
3					
6					
4					

12

Name _____

Multiplying

> Write the missing numbers.

1. 100 × 71 = ⟨ 7100 ⟩

⟨ 99 ⟩ × 71 = 7029

2. 100 × 36 = ⟨ ⟩

⟨ ⟩ × 36 = 3708

3. 100 × 46 = ⟨ ⟩

⟨ ⟩ × 46 = 4508

4. 100 × 27 = ⟨ ⟩

⟨ ⟩ × 27 = 2754

5. 100 × 78 = ⟨ ⟩

⟨ ⟩ × 78 = 7644

6. 100 × 39 = ⟨ ⟩

101 × 39 = ⟨ ⟩

7. 100 × 65 = ⟨ ⟩

99 × 65 = ⟨ ⟩

8. 100 × 35 = ⟨ ⟩

⟨ ⟩ × 35 = 3605

9. 100 × 62 = ⟨ ⟩

⟨ ⟩ × 62 = 6014

10. 100 × 36 = ⟨ ⟩

98 × 36 = ⟨ ⟩

11. 100 × 31 = ⟨ ⟩

103 × 31 = ⟨ ⟩

12. 100 × 19 = ⟨ ⟩

95 × 19 = ⟨ ⟩

Dice multiplying

Throw two dice to make a 2-digit number.

Write it down and complete the multiplication.

Two dice

1. [|] × 10 =

2. [|] × 100 =

3. [|] × 20 =

4. [|] × 50 =

5. [|] × 19 =

6. [|] × 21 =

7. [|] × 101 =

8. [|] × 99 =

9. [|] × 18 =

10. [|] × 102 =

11. [|] × 22 =

12. [|] × 98 =

13. [|] × 31 =

14. [|] × 49 =

15. [|] × 39 =

16. [|] × 61 =

Name _____

Multiplying by doubling

Complete these.

1. $7 \times 6 =$ _____    $7 \times 12 =$ _____

2. $8 \times 9 =$ _____ $8 \times 18 =$ _____

3. $6 \times 7 =$ _____    $6 \times 14 =$ _____

4. $4 \times 8 =$ _____    $4 \times 16 =$ _____

5. $9 \times 6 =$ _____    $9 \times 12 =$ _____

6. $3 \times 9 =$ _____    $3 \times 36 =$ _____

7. $9 \times 8 =$ _____    $9 \times 32 =$ _____

8. $5 \times 7 =$ _____    $5 \times 28 =$ _____

9. $8 \times 6 =$ _____ $8 \times 24 =$ _____

10. $7 \times 4 =$ _____ $7 \times 16 =$ _____

11. $11 \times 7 =$ _____    $11 \times 14 =$ _____

12. $6 \times 6 =$ _____ $6 \times 48 =$ _____

Name _____

Fraction wheels

Write the fractions of the amounts in the outer circles of the wheels.

1.

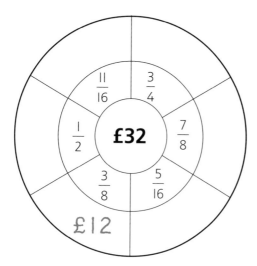

£32 — $\frac{11}{16}$, $\frac{3}{4}$, $\frac{1}{2}$, $\frac{7}{8}$, $\frac{3}{8}$, $\frac{5}{16}$ — £12

2.

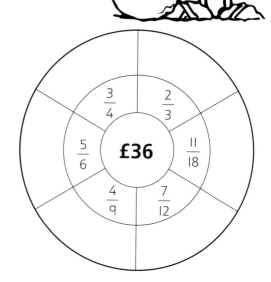

£36 — $\frac{3}{4}$, $\frac{2}{3}$, $\frac{5}{6}$, $\frac{11}{18}$, $\frac{4}{9}$, $\frac{7}{12}$

3.

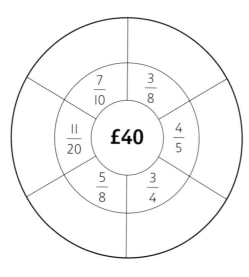

£40 — $\frac{7}{10}$, $\frac{3}{8}$, $\frac{11}{20}$, $\frac{4}{5}$, $\frac{5}{8}$, $\frac{3}{4}$

4.

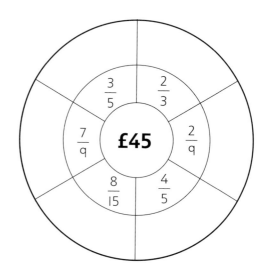

£45 — $\frac{3}{5}$, $\frac{2}{3}$, $\frac{7}{9}$, $\frac{2}{9}$, $\frac{8}{15}$, $\frac{4}{5}$

5.

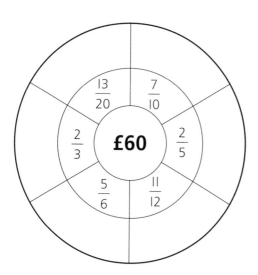

£60 — $\frac{13}{20}$, $\frac{7}{10}$, $\frac{2}{3}$, $\frac{2}{5}$, $\frac{5}{6}$, $\frac{11}{12}$

6.

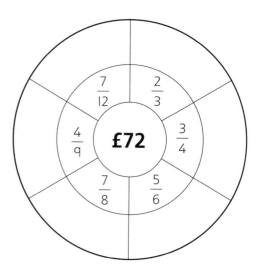

£72 — $\frac{7}{12}$, $\frac{2}{3}$, $\frac{4}{9}$, $\frac{3}{4}$, $\frac{7}{8}$, $\frac{5}{6}$

Name _____

Equivalent fractions

Write the missing numbers.

1. $\dfrac{1}{2}$ = $\dfrac{\boxed{}}{4}$ = $\dfrac{3}{\boxed{}}$ = $\dfrac{\boxed{}}{8}$ = $\dfrac{\boxed{}}{14}$

2. $\dfrac{1}{5}$ = $\dfrac{\boxed{}}{10}$ = $\dfrac{\boxed{}}{15}$ = $\dfrac{5}{\boxed{}}$ = $\dfrac{6}{\boxed{}}$

3. $\dfrac{3}{4}$ = $\dfrac{6}{\boxed{}}$ = $\dfrac{\boxed{}}{12}$ = $\dfrac{12}{\boxed{}}$ = $\dfrac{\boxed{}}{24}$

4. $\dfrac{2}{3}$ = $\dfrac{\boxed{}}{6}$ = $\dfrac{6}{\boxed{}}$ = $\dfrac{\boxed{}}{12}$ = $\dfrac{10}{\boxed{}}$

5. $\dfrac{3}{5}$ = $\dfrac{\boxed{}}{10}$ = $\dfrac{\boxed{}}{15}$ = $\dfrac{12}{\boxed{}}$ = $\dfrac{18}{\boxed{}}$

6. $\dfrac{3}{10}$ = $\dfrac{\boxed{}}{20}$ = $\dfrac{9}{\boxed{}}$ = $\dfrac{\boxed{}}{40}$ = $\dfrac{\boxed{}}{50}$

7. $\dfrac{1}{4}$ = $\dfrac{2}{\boxed{}}$ = $\dfrac{\boxed{}}{16}$ = $\dfrac{5}{\boxed{}}$ = $\dfrac{10}{\boxed{}}$

Equivalent fractions

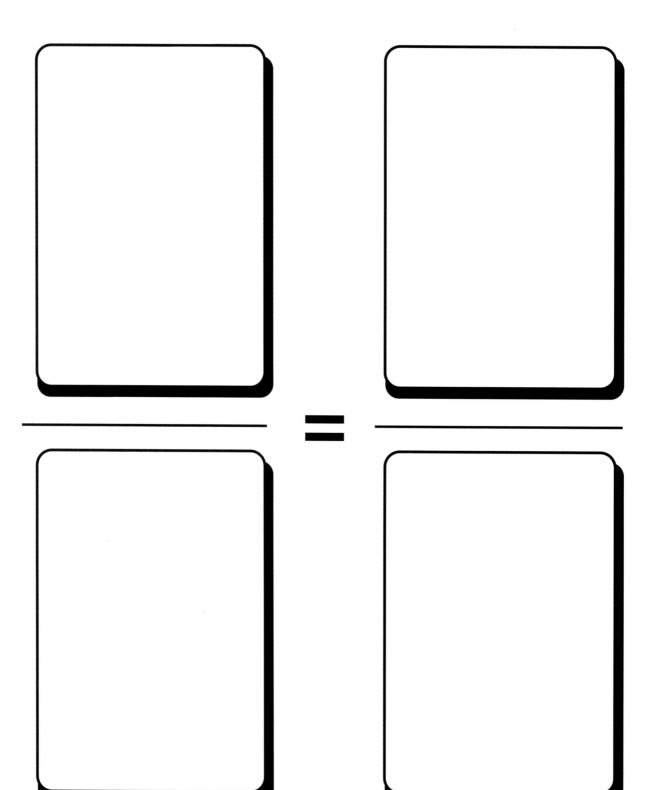

Teacher's instructions
A game for two or more players, each with a copy of this scoresheet.
Shuffle the cards and deal five each. Place the rest in a pile, face down.
On your turn, discard one card and pick up the top card from the pile.
The winner is the first who can place four cards on their sheet to show a pair
of equivalent fractions.

Materials
4 sets of number
cards (1 to 10)

Name _____

Reducing fractions

Write these fractions in their simplest forms.

1. $\dfrac{8}{12}$ = _____

2. $\dfrac{6}{10}$ = _____

3. $\dfrac{4}{16}$ = _____

4. $\dfrac{4}{32}$ = _____

5. $\dfrac{4}{6}$ = _____

6. $\dfrac{9}{12}$ = _____

7. $\dfrac{21}{24}$ = _____

8. $\dfrac{8}{10}$ = _____

9. $\dfrac{12}{32}$ = _____

10. $\dfrac{2}{6}$ = _____

11. $\dfrac{25}{40}$ = _____

12. $\dfrac{15}{50}$ = _____

13. $\dfrac{42}{60}$ = _____

14. $\dfrac{15}{20}$ = _____

15. $\dfrac{4}{10}$ = _____

16. $\dfrac{18}{45}$ = _____

17. $\dfrac{24}{40}$ = _____

18. $\dfrac{7}{42}$ = _____

19. $\dfrac{63}{90}$ = _____

20. $\dfrac{20}{24}$ = _____

21. $\dfrac{14}{24}$ = _____

22. $\dfrac{75}{100}$ = _____

23. $\dfrac{33}{36}$ = _____

24. $\dfrac{22}{50}$ = _____

Name _____

Ordering fractions

> Estimate the order of each set of fractions, smallest to largest, by writing the letters from top to bottom.

> Convert each fraction to one with the given common denominator.

> Write the correct order. Compare with your estimated order.

1.

Estimated order					

A $\frac{2}{3} = \frac{\square}{24}$ B $\frac{3}{4} = \frac{\square}{24}$

C $\frac{1}{2} = \frac{\square}{24}$ D $\frac{5}{6} = \frac{\square}{24}$

E $\frac{3}{8} = \frac{\square}{24}$

Correct order					

2.

Estimated order					

A $\frac{3}{4} = \frac{\square}{20}$ B $\frac{1}{2} = \frac{\square}{20}$

C $\frac{1}{4} = \frac{\square}{20}$ D $\frac{4}{5} = \frac{\square}{20}$

E $\frac{7}{10} = \frac{\square}{20}$

Correct order					

3.

Estimated order					

A $\frac{3}{5} = \frac{\square}{30}$ B $\frac{5}{6} = \frac{\square}{30}$

C $\frac{1}{2} = \frac{\square}{30}$ D $\frac{2}{3} = \frac{\square}{30}$

E $\frac{11}{15} = \frac{\square}{30}$

Correct order					

4.

Estimated order					

A $\frac{2}{5} = \frac{\square}{100}$ B $\frac{7}{20} = \frac{\square}{100}$

C $\frac{3}{10} = \frac{\square}{100}$ D $\frac{1}{4} = \frac{\square}{100}$

E $\frac{8}{25} = \frac{\square}{100}$

Correct order					

19

Name _____

Comparing fractions

For each pair, write equivalent fractions with the same denominator.

Write < or > between them.

1.
$\frac{2}{3}$ → $\frac{4}{6}$ > $\frac{1}{2}$ → $\frac{3}{6}$

2.
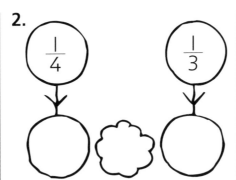
$\frac{1}{4}$ $\frac{1}{3}$

3.
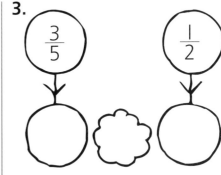
$\frac{3}{5}$ $\frac{1}{2}$

4.
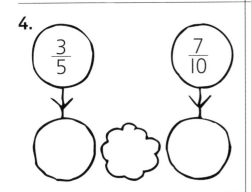
$\frac{3}{5}$ $\frac{7}{10}$

5.
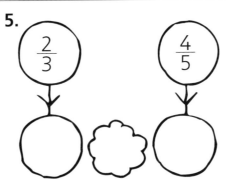
$\frac{2}{3}$ $\frac{4}{5}$

6.
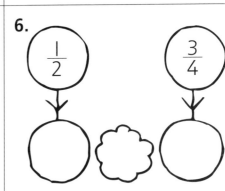
$\frac{1}{2}$ $\frac{3}{4}$

7.
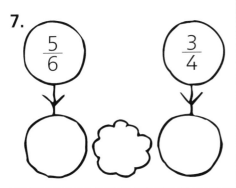
$\frac{5}{6}$ $\frac{3}{4}$

8.
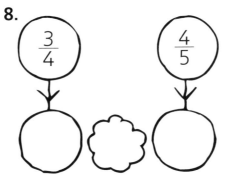
$\frac{3}{4}$ $\frac{4}{5}$

9.
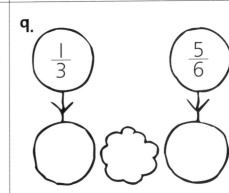
$\frac{1}{3}$ $\frac{5}{6}$

10.
$\frac{5}{6}$ $\frac{11}{12}$

11.
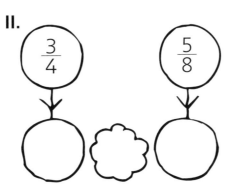
$\frac{3}{4}$ $\frac{5}{8}$

12.
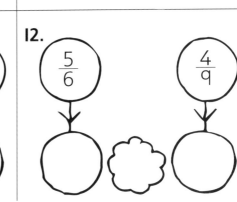
$\frac{5}{6}$ $\frac{4}{9}$

Name _____

Adding to 1000

Decide what you need to add to each number to make 1000.

Write the number in the matching space.

600	100	400
300	250	850
750	350	500

Makes
→
1000

400		

140	830	370
510	260	690
720	480	910

Makes
→
1000

437	907	256
596	475	328
843	666	172

Makes
→
1000

Name _____

Car mileage

> Write what distance must be travelled to make the next ten.

	car mileage				next ten
1.	324·6	+	5·4	=	330·0
2.	108·3	+		=	
3.	15·4	+		=	
4.	260·5	+		=	
5.	371·9	+		=	
6.	428·7	+		=	

> Write the original mileage.

	car mileage				next ten
7.		+	5·4	=	40·0
8.		+	2·7	=	120·0
9.		+	6·4	=	70·0
10.		+	8·3	=	350·0
11.		+	7·2	=	900·0
12.		+	1·5	=	280·0

Name _____

The next whole number

0·63

12·84

6·31

7·72

7·28

1·23

3·59

4·35

8·95

2·75

5·33

0·15

6·46

9·79

11·52

4·09

3·14

8·46

9·06

5·66

Teacher's instructions
A game for two or three players. Cover each ship with a counter. Take turns to uncover a number, then say (a) the next whole number, (b) what must be added to make it. Check each other's answers. If correct, collect a cube. When all the counters have been removed, see who has the most cubes.

Materials
Counters
Cubes

23

Name _____

Adding several numbers

Write the missing numbers.

Totals

11	29	9	17	〇
32	25	19	27	〇
34	28	21	52	〇
46	26	37	15	〇
〇	〇	〇	〇	

Totals

23	37	9	27	〇
8	24	35	25	〇
28	21	36	18	〇
34	26	19	29	〇
〇	〇	〇	〇	

Totals

15		7	21	66
8	24		16	80
	6	19	9	56
17	25	31		96
〇	〇	〇	〇	

Totals

19	33	21		89
23		18	32	97
15	36		41	114
	17	31	14	87
〇	〇	〇	〇	

24

Difference tables

Complete these difference tables.

d	178	347	465	218
129				
364				
289				
542				

d	29	179	17	358
453				
13				
562				
26				

Name _____

Multiples

Write the missing multiples in each list.

I. multiples of 3

2. multiples of 7

3. multiples of 4

4. multiples of 9

5. multiples of 5

6. multiples of 6

7. multiples of 8

8. multiples of 15

q. multiples of 20

10. multiples of 12

Name _____

Common multiples

12	20	18	36
10	70	30	60
28	8	56	12
25	48	9	42
72	6	27	12
32	54	16	36

Teacher's instructions
A game for two pairs of players. Take turns to deal out two cards to a pair. If possible, place a counter on a number which is a common multiple of both card numbers. Otherwise do nothing. You cannot place a counter on a number that is already covered. Shuffle the cards each time. The winner is the first pair to have four counters in any one row or column.

Materials
Number cards (2 to 10)
A set of counters each

27

Name _____

Lowest common multiple

Write a number in each square that is the smallest multiple of both the row and column headings.

1.

	2	3	5
4			
6			
7			

2.

	2	7	8
5			
3			
q			

3.

	4	5	6
3			
7			
8			

4.

	8	2	7
5			
q			
6			

Name _____

Dividing by 3

Place a tick beside each number that can be divided exactly by 3.

1. | 29 | |

2. | 35 | |

3. | 46 | |

4. | 82 | |

5. | 91 | |

6. | 135 | |

7. | 248 | |

8. | 369 | |

9. | 172 | |

10. | 451 | |

11. | 219 | |

12. | 1327 | |

Place a tick beside each number that can be divided exactly by 6.

13. | 536 | |

14. | 248 | |

15. | 318 | |

16. | 416 | |

17. | 524 | |

18. | 369 | |

19. | 384 | |

20. | 168 | |

21. | 357 | |

22. | 408 | |

23. | 591 | |

24. | 621 | |

Name _____

Divisibility

Put ticks in the table to show which numbers divide into the numbers on the left.

Write your own six numbers underneath with their ticks.

	÷2	÷3	÷4	÷5	÷6	÷8	÷9	÷10
40	✔		✔					
54								
68								
84								
92								
112								
235								
468								

Name _____

Multiplying decimals by 10

Complete the wall.

1. 2·3 × 10 =

2. 4·5 × 10 =

3. 0·7 × 10 =

4. 4·0 × 10 =

5. 3·7 × 10 =

6. 17·2 × 10 =

7. 23·4 × 10 =

8. 15·6 × 10 =

9. 7·3 × 10 =

10. 5·4 × 10 =

11. 0·6 × 10 =

12. 3·3 × 10 =

Name _____

Multiplying decimals by 100

Write each length in centimetres.

1.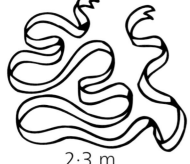

2·3 m

[ ] cm

2.

1·7 m

[ ] cm

3.

6 m

[ ] cm

4.

4·8 m

[ ] cm

5.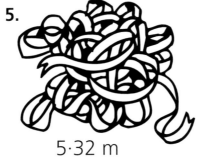

5·32 m

[ ] cm

6.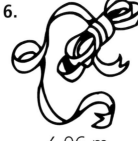

4·06 m

[ ] cm

7.

7·00 m

[ ] cm

8.

$8\frac{1}{2}$ m

[ ] cm

9.

1·39 m

[ ] cm

Name _____

Multiplying decimals by 10 and 100

Write the missing numbers.

1. ⬭ $\times 10 = 24\cdot0$

2. ⬭ $\times 10 = 36\cdot0$

3. ⬭ $\times 10 = 47\cdot0$

4. $5\cdot3 \times$ ⬭ $= 53\cdot0$

5. $0\cdot4 \times$ ⬭ $= 4\cdot0$

6. ⬭ $\times 10 = 70\cdot0$

7. $3\cdot5 \times$ ⬭ $= 350\cdot0$

8. ⬭ $\times 100 = 180\cdot0$

9. ⬭ $\times 100 = 472\cdot0$

10. ⬭ $\times 100 = 536\cdot0$

11. $7\cdot29 \times$ ⬭ $= 72\cdot9$

12. ⬭ $\times 10 = 127\cdot0$

13. ⬭ $\times 10 = 146\cdot0$

14. ⬭ $\times 10 = 35\cdot6$

15. $10 \times$ ⬭ $= 38\cdot0$

16. $10 \times$ ⬭ $= 49\cdot0$

17. $100 \times$ ⬭ $= 381\cdot0$

18. $100 \times$ ⬭ $= 46\cdot5$

33

Abacus Ginn and Company 2001. Copying permitted for purchasing school only. This material is not copyright free.

Name _____

Dividing decimals by 10 and 100

Write the number in the place-value boards to complete each division.

	Th	H	T	U	t	h	
1.		1	2	3			÷ 10 =
2.			4	7	6		÷ 10 =
3.			5	8			÷ 100 =
4.				9	7		÷ 10 =
5.			1	9			÷ 100 =
6.	4	6	0	0			÷ 1000 =
7.		5	0	1			÷ 10 =
8.				0	6		÷ 10 =
9.			1	1	3		÷ 100 =
10.				8			÷ 10 =
11.			7	6	1		÷ 10 =
12.				3			÷ 100 =
13.							÷ 10 =
14.							÷ 100 =
15.							÷ 10 =

H	T	U	t	h	th
		6	3	5	
		0	7		
		1	3	8	

Name _____

Target multiplication

Target	Multiplication			Product	Score (difference)
200	☐	×	☐☐ =		
160	☐	×	☐☐ =		
280	☐	×	☐☐ =		
95	☐	×	☐☐ =		
145	☐	×	☐☐ =		
430	☐	×	☐☐ =		
350	☐	×	☐☐ =		
190	☐	×	☐☐ =		
100	☐	×	☐☐ =		
495	☐	×	☐☐ =		
				Total score	

Teacher's instructions
Shuffle the cards and deal out three.
Arrange them to make a multiplication of a 2-digit number and a 1-digit number. Try to get as close as you can to the target. Score the difference.
Replace the cards, reshuffle them, and repeat for the next target.

Materials
Number cards (1 to 9)

Name _____

Dice multiplying

Roll a dice to find the multiplying number, then multiply.

If you roll a 'I', then roll again.

A dice

| 4 | × 314 = (1200) + (40) + (16) = ___1256___ |

1. ☐ × 143 = (____) + (____) + (____) = _____

2. ☐ × 265 = (____) + (____) + (____) = _____

3. ☐ × 371 = (____) + (____) + (____) = _____

4. ☐ × 536 = (____) + (____) + (____) = _____

5. ☐ × 219 = (____) + (____) + (____) = _____

6. ☐ × 391 = (____) + (____) + (____) = _____

7. ☐ × 644 = (____) + (____) + (____) = _____

8. ☐ × 832 = (____) + (____) + (____) = _____

9. ☐ × 258 = (____) + (____) + (____) = _____

10. ☐ × 444 = (____) + (____) + (____) = _____

Name _____

Multiplying by 11

Complete these multiplications.

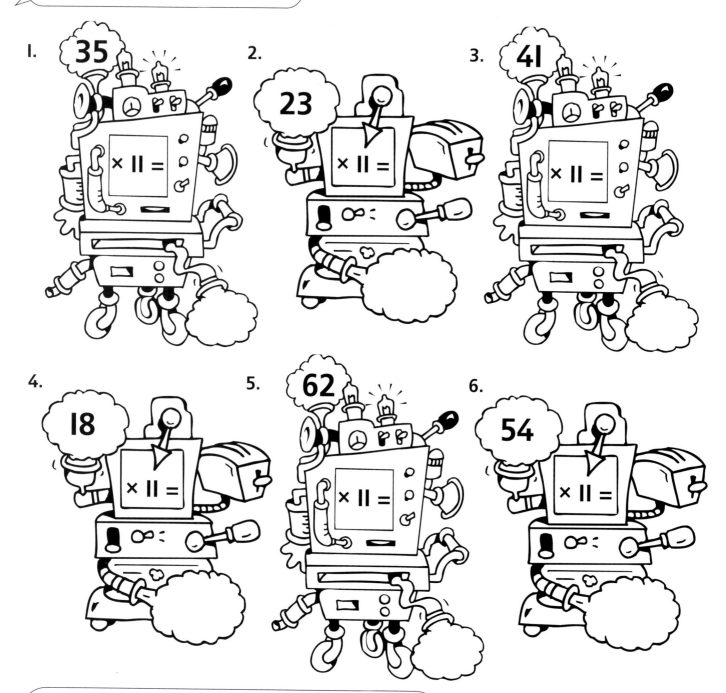

1. 35 × 11 =

2. 23 × 11 =

3. 41 × 11 =

4. 18 × 11 =

5. 62 × 11 =

6. 54 × 11 =

Try some of your own numbers multiplied by 11.

Write about any patterns you notice.

Can you find a quick way of multiplying a 2-digit number by 11?

Name _____

Multiplying

Roll a dice to find the multiplying number, then multiply.

If you roll a 'I', then roll again.

A dice

1.
（ ）

I	5	2	6
×		☐	

2.
（ ）

2	7	3	4
×		☐	

3.
（ ）

4	I	6	3
×		☐	

4.
（ ）

5	3	2	I
×		☐	

5.
（ ）

2	7	I	6
×		☐	

6.
（ ）

3	8	4	7
×		☐	

Name _____

Multiplying game

round 1

score

round 2

score

round 3

score

round 4

score

Teacher's instructions
A game for two or more players, each with a copy of this scoresheet.
Throw the dice five times in each round. After each throw, each write the
number in one of your boxes. Complete the multiplication. Check each
other's multiplications, using a calculator if necessary. The player with the
largest answer scores 4 points, the next largest 3 points, and so on.
The winner is the player with the most points after four rounds.

Materials
A dice
A calculator

Name _____

Multiplying

Complete these.

I. ⬡

$$
\begin{array}{r}
3\ \ 2\ \ 6 \\
\times\ \ \ 4\ \ 2 \\
\hline
\end{array}
$$

_____

_____

2. ⬡

$$
\begin{array}{r}
3\ \ 2\ \ 6 \\
\times\ \ \ 2\ \ 7 \\
\hline
\end{array}
$$

_____

_____

3. ⬡

$$
\begin{array}{r}
4\ \ 9\ \ 6 \\
\times\ \ \ 3\ \ 2 \\
\hline
\end{array}
$$

_____

_____

4. ⬡

$$
\begin{array}{r}
2\ \ 7\ \ 1 \\
\times\ \ \ 5\ \ 3 \\
\hline
\end{array}
$$

_____

_____

5. ⬡

$$
\begin{array}{r}
1\ \ 8\ \ 6 \\
\times\ \ \ 6\ \ 4 \\
\hline
\end{array}
$$

_____

_____

6. ⬡

$$
\begin{array}{r}
7\ \ 2\ \ 5 \\
\times\ \ \ 1\ \ 9 \\
\hline
\end{array}
$$

_____

_____

Name _____

Calculations

$4 \cdot 8 \times 6 = 28 \cdot 8$

$26 \cdot 6 \div 7 = 3 \cdot 8$

$7 \cdot 6 \times 13 = 98 \cdot 8$

$75 \times 14 = 1050$

$323 \div 19 = 17$

$12 \times 5 \cdot 4 = 64 \cdot 8$

$53 \cdot 6 \div 8 = 6 \cdot 7$

Use the eight calculations above to help you write calculations with these answers.

1. 13 = $\underline{98 \cdot 8 \div 7 \cdot 6}$ 2. 7·6 = _____

3. 19 = _____ 4. 53·6 = _____

5. 26·6 = _____ 6. 14 = _____

7. 4·8 = _____ 8. 5·4 = _____

9. 53·1 = _____ 10. 75 = _____

11. 9 = _____ 12. 7 = _____

13. 12 = _____ 14. 323 = _____

15. 8 = _____ 16. 6 = _____

Abacus Ginn and Company 2001. Copying permitted for purchasing school only. This material is not copyright free.

Name _____

Remainder game

25   19   32   63

33   42   31   54

39   58   33   41

45   21   26   43

27   61   57   38

47   46   17   65

Teacher's instructions
A game for two or three players.
Take turns to remove a counter and reveal a number. Cover each number with a counter.
Roll the dice for the dividing number. If you roll a '1', roll again.
Say the result of the division, giving the remainder as a fraction in its lowest terms. Check
each other's answers. If you are correct, keep the counter. If not, replace it. If your division is
exact, with no remainder, then you replace the counter.
When all the numbers have been revealed, the winner is the player with the most counters.

Materials
A dice
A set of counters

42

Name _____

Remainders

Complete each division, giving the remainder as a fraction.

Write each fraction in its simplest form.

I.	$32 \div 3 =$ _____	2.	$14 \div 5 =$ _____
3.	$73 \div 2 =$ _____	4.	$65 \div 4 =$ _____
5.	$51 \div 6 =$ _____	6.	$19 \div 3 =$ _____
7.	$36 \div 5 =$ _____	8.	$29 \div 4 =$ _____
9.	$87 \div 8 =$ _____	10.	$23 \div 9 =$ _____
II.	$51 \div 2 =$ _____	12.	$49 \div 5 =$ _____
13.	$33 \div 6 =$ _____	14.	$28 \div 3 =$ _____
15.	$62 \div 5 =$ _____	16.	$92 \div 8 =$ _____
17.	$31 \div 4 =$ _____	18.	$73 \div 7 =$ _____
19.	$55 \div 8 =$ _____	20.	$6 \div 9 =$ _____

Name _____

Improper fractions

Write the missing numbers.

1. $4\frac{3}{4}$ = $\dfrac{\boxed{}}{4}$

2. $1\frac{5}{6}$ = $\dfrac{\boxed{}}{6}$

3. $2\dfrac{\boxed{}}{5}$ = $\dfrac{13}{5}$

4. $\boxed{}\frac{1}{2}$ = $\dfrac{11}{2}$

5. $3\dfrac{\boxed{}}{7}$ = $\dfrac{24}{7}$

6. $7\frac{2}{3}$ = $\dfrac{\boxed{}}{3}$

7. $\boxed{}\frac{5}{8}$ = $\dfrac{45}{8}$

8. $10\frac{1}{6}$ = $\dfrac{\boxed{}}{6}$

9. $2\dfrac{\boxed{}}{3}$ = $\dfrac{7}{3}$

10. $\boxed{}\frac{4}{9}$ = $\dfrac{13}{9}$

11. $9\frac{4}{5}$ = $\dfrac{\boxed{}}{5}$

12. $13\frac{1}{2}$ = $\dfrac{\boxed{}}{2}$

13. $15\dfrac{\boxed{}}{9}$ = $\dfrac{142}{9}$

14. $16\dfrac{\boxed{}}{7}$ = $\dfrac{115}{7}$

15. $\boxed{}\frac{3}{4}$ = $\dfrac{31}{4}$

16. $9\dfrac{\boxed{}}{8}$ = $\dfrac{79}{8}$

17. $11\frac{3}{10}$ = $\dfrac{\boxed{}}{10}$

18. $4\frac{6}{7}$ = $\dfrac{\boxed{}}{7}$

44

Name _____

Hundredths

Write a decimal in each box to match the position on the line.

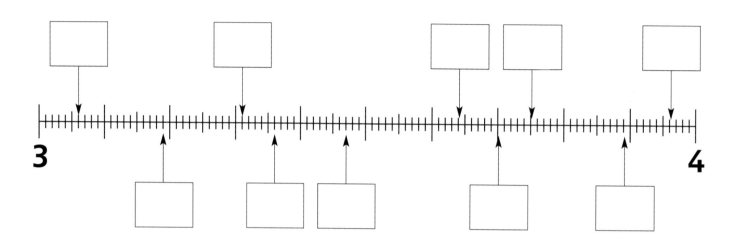

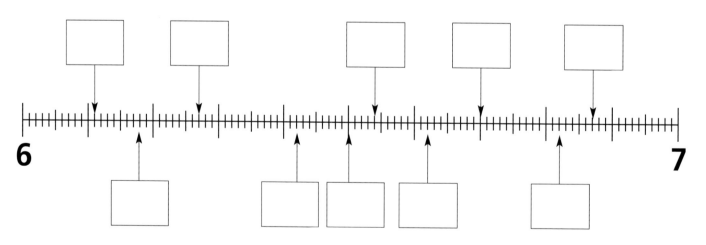

Abacus Ginn and Company 2001. Copying permitted for purchasing school only. This material is not copyright free.

Name _____

Hundredths

Choose three of these cards to make a decimal number between 0 and I.

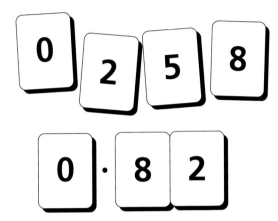

Mark its position on the number line.

Mark the positions of all the other possible numbers.

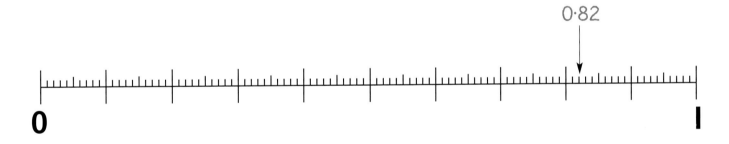

Now choose three from these to make numbers between 2 and 3.

Mark the positions of numbers on the number line.

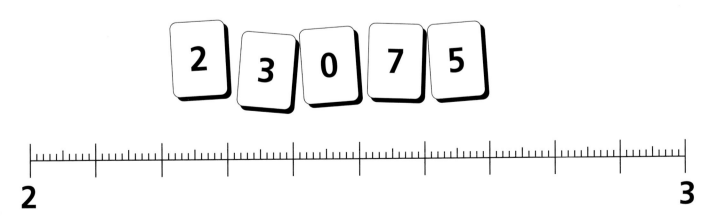

46

Name _____

Ordering hundredths

Write < or > between each pair.

1. $1\cdot63$ ⬜ $1\cdot36$

2. $4\cdot36$ ⬜ $4\cdot63$

3. $2\cdot35$ ⬜ $3\cdot25$

4. $3\frac{12}{100}$ ⬜ $3\cdot21$

5. $0\cdot5$ ⬜ $\frac{40}{100}$

6. $1\cdot3$ ⬜ $1\frac{27}{100}$

7. $4\cdot07$ ⬜ $4\cdot60$

8. $4\frac{11}{100}$ ⬜ $4\cdot1$

9. $5\cdot26$ ⬜ $5\cdot3$

10. $6\cdot4$ ⬜ $6\cdot39$

11. $8\frac{1}{100}$ ⬜ $8\cdot1$

12. $7\cdot35$ ⬜ $5\cdot37$

13. $4\cdot09$ ⬜ $4\cdot90$

14. $6\cdot5$ ⬜ $6\cdot51$

15. $3\cdot89$ ⬜ $3\cdot9$

16. $7\cdot25$ ⬜ 8

17. $3\cdot7$ ⬜ $4\cdot01$

18. $5\frac{11}{100}$ ⬜ $5\cdot1$

47

Name _____

Adding 5-digit numbers

round 1

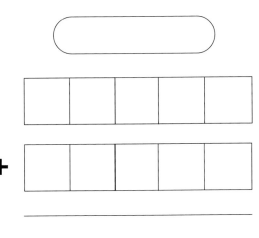

round 2

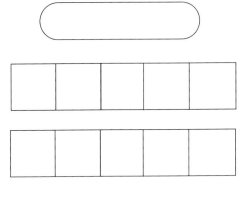

round 3

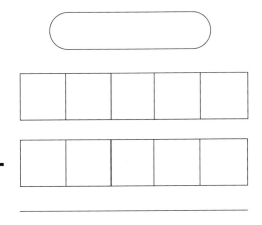

round 4

Teacher's instructions
A game for two or more players, each with a copy of this scoresheet.
Throw the dice ten times in each round. After each throw, each write
the number in one of your boxes. After the tenth throw add the numbers
together. Check each other's additions, using a calculator if necessary.
The player with the largest answer scores 4 points, the next largest 3 points,
and so on.
The winner is the player with the most points after four rounds.

Materials
A dice
A calculator

48

Adding 4-digit and 5-digit numbers

Estimate the total, then add.

1.
```
    3  2  1  6
 +  4  5  3  2
 _____
```

2.
```
    7  3  2  5
 +  1  6  4  8
 _____
```

3.
```
    2  9  5  3
 +  3  7  4  8
 _____
```

4.
```
    5  3  6  4  2
 +     4  7  1  9
 _____
```

5.
```
    4  8  2  3  7
 +     1  9  5  8
 _____
```

6.
```
    1  7  3  2  6
 +     5  4  9  6
 _____
```

7.
```
       4  3  1  7
 +  2  8  6  5  9
 _____
```

8.
```
       4  5  4  9
 +  3  2  6  0  8
 _____
```

9.
```
       5  9  0  7
 +  2  0  3  7  5
 _____
```

10.
```
    3  1  5  8  6
 +  4  2  3  7  9
 _____
```

11.
```
    5  8  2  1  9
 +  4  0  1  5  8
 _____
```

12.
```
    3  2  3  9  6
 +  1  0  7  8  8
 _____
```

Name _____

Adding decimal numbers

| 4·7 | 2·9 | 5·7 | 1·4 | 2·6 | 3·8 | 0·5 |

8·5	6·4	7·1	3·4	7·3
5·2	7·6	4·6	9·5	6·75
1·9	6·1	5·2	10·4	3·1
8·6	3·8	4·35	7·4	6·2
4·3	4·0	9·6	8·3	5·5

Teacher's instructions
A game for two players.
Take turns to choose two number cards. Add the numbers together. If the answer
appears on the board, cover it with one of your counters. You cannot place a
counter on a number that is already covered. Check each other's additions.
The winner is the first to place four counters in a straight line.

Materials
A set of counters each

50

Name _____

Adding decimal numbers

Estimate the total, then add.

1.
```
    5 · 2  6
  + 1 · 3  7
```

2.
```
    4 · 3  5
  + 2 · 4  6
```

3.
```
    5 · 3  9
  + 6 · 4  8
```

4.
```
    7 · 0  9
  + 5 · 3  6
```

5.
```
    2 · 8  7
  + 1 · 9  4
```

6.
```
    5 · 7  6
  + 6 · 7  5
```

7.
```
    4 · 5  2
  + 6 · 7  3
```

8.
```
    8 · 4  6
  + 1 · 7  2
```

9.
```
    5 · 3  6
  + 3 · 8  1
```

10.
```
    2 · 7  8
  + 1 · 4  6
```

11.
```
    3 · 5  9
  + 1 · 7  6
```

12.
```
    2 · 8  3
  + 1 · 9  7
```

Name _____

Adding decimal numbers

Add the two next-door numbers.   Write the total above.

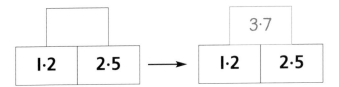

Complete these.

1.

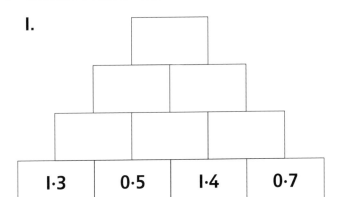

| 1·3 | 0·5 | 1·4 | 0·7 |

2.

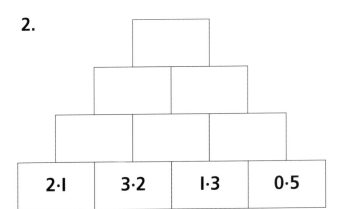

| 2·1 | 3·2 | 1·3 | 0·5 |

3.

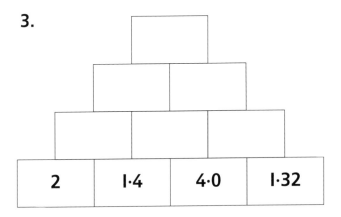

| 2 | 1·4 | 4·0 | 1·32 |

4.

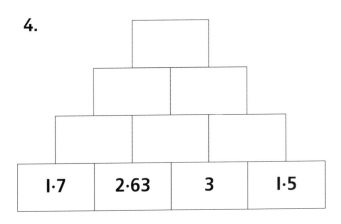

| 1·7 | 2·63 | 3 | 1·5 |

5.

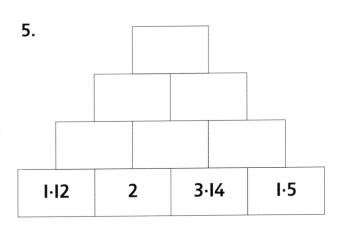

| 1·12 | 2 | 3·14 | 1·5 |

6.

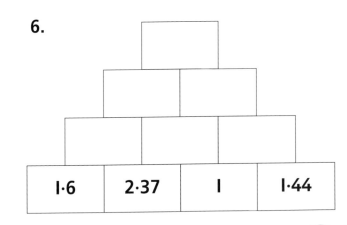

| 1·6 | 2·37 | 1 | 1·44 |

Name _____

Taking away

Estimate, then subtract.

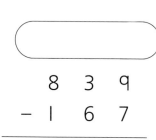

1. ⬭
```
    5   1   8
 -  3   7   3
 _____
```
_____

2. ⬭
```
    8   3   9
 -  1   6   7
 _____
```
_____

3. ⬭
```
    6   2   5
 -  2   5   2
 _____
```
_____

4. ⬭
```
    7   4   7
 -  5   8   3
 _____
```
_____

5. ⬭
```
    9   5   2
 -  4   7   6
 _____
```
_____

6. ⬭
```
    7   1   1
 -  3   5   4
 _____
```
_____

7. ⬭
```
    6   3   3
 -  2   9   7
 _____
```
_____

8. ⬭
```
    5   4   5
 -  1   6   8
 _____
```
_____

Subtraction game

round 1

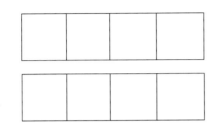

score

round 2

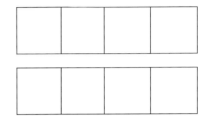

score

round 3

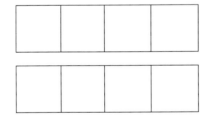

score

round 4

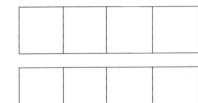

score

Total score

Teacher's instructions
A game for two or more players, each with a copy of this scoresheet.
Throw the dice eight times in each round. After each throw, all the players write the
number in one of their boxes. After the eighth throw, the players subtract the bottom
number from the top one (checking each other's work).
If the top number is smaller than the bottom number, score 0 points.
Otherwise, score the answer. The winner is the one with the most points after
four rounds.

Materials
A dice

54

Name _____

Ordering subtractions

Cut out these subtraction cards.

Put them in a straight line in order of your estimated answers, smallest to largest.

Complete the subtractions to check the order.

4 1 6 3 − 2 8 2 7 ――――― ―――――	3 9 5 8 − 1 7 4 6 ――――― ―――――	9 7 6 0 − 5 4 0 9 ――――― ―――――
5 3 8 1 − 1 2 5 6 ――――― ―――――	6 3 0 9 − 4 5 8 2 ――――― ―――――	4 3 8 2 − 1 7 5 1 ――――― ―――――
7 4 9 7 − 2 8 6 2 ――――― ―――――	8 9 4 2 − 4 0 8 9 ――――― ―――――	6 5 4 3 − 3 9 0 6 ――――― ―――――
6 3 5 9 − 2 8 5 6 ――――― ―――――	7 2 7 5 − 4 4 9 3 ――――― ―――――	8 6 7 1 − 4 7 2 5 ――――― ―――――

55

Abacus Ginn and Company 2001. Copying permitted for purchasing school only. This material is not copyright free.

Name _____

Subtracting decimals

Complete these.

1. ◯

$$
\begin{array}{r}
4 \cdot 3\ \ 6 \\
-\ 1 \cdot 4\ \ 9 \\
\hline
\end{array}
$$

2. ◯

$$
\begin{array}{r}
2 \cdot 5\ \ 4 \\
-\ 1 \cdot 7\ \ 7 \\
\hline
\end{array}
$$

3. ◯

$$
\begin{array}{r}
3 \cdot 2\ \ 9 \\
-\ 2 \cdot 5\ \ 4 \\
\hline
\end{array}
$$

4. ◯

$$
\begin{array}{r}
1 \cdot 3\ \ 6 \\
-\ 0 \cdot 4\ \ 8 \\
\hline
\end{array}
$$

5. ◯

$$
\begin{array}{r}
9 \cdot 2\ \ 7 \\
-\ 3 \cdot 6\ \ 9 \\
\hline
\end{array}
$$

6. ◯

$$
\begin{array}{r}
6 \cdot 5\ \ 8 \\
-\ 5 \cdot 7\ \ 9 \\
\hline
\end{array}
$$

7. ◯

$$
\begin{array}{r}
5 \cdot 3\ \ 4 \\
-\ 2 \cdot 8\ \ 8 \\
\hline
\end{array}
$$

8. ◯

$$
\begin{array}{r}
7 \cdot 0\ \ 5 \\
-\ 4 \cdot 2\ \ 9 \\
\hline
\end{array}
$$

Subtracting decimals game

round 1

☐ . ☐☐

− ☐ . ☐☐

_____

_____

score ☐

round 2

☐ . ☐☐

− ☐ . ☐☐

_____

_____

score ☐

round 3

☐ . ☐☐

− ☐ . ☐☐

_____

_____

score ☐

round 4

☐ . ☐☐

− ☐ . ☐☐

_____

_____

score ☐

Total score ☐

Teacher's instructions

A game for two or more players, each with a copy of this scoresheet.
Throw the dice six times in each round. After each throw, all the players write the
number in one of their boxes. After the sixth throw, the players subtract the bottom
number from the top one (checking each other's work). If the top number is smaller
than the bottom number, score 0 points. Otherwise, score the answer.
The winner is the player with the most points after four rounds.

Materials
A dice

57

Name _____

Subtracting decimals

Cut out these subtraction cards.

Put them in a straight line in order of your estimated answers, smallest to largest.

Complete the subtractions to check the order.

$3 \cdot 2 \ 8$ $- \ 1 \cdot 4 \ 7$	$4 \cdot 5 \ 6$ $- \ 2 \cdot 6 \ 8$	$2 \cdot 3 \ 4$ $- \ 0 \cdot 7 \ 7$	$9 \cdot 8 \ 6$ $- \ 4 \cdot 9 \ 5$
$7 \cdot 4 \ 1$ $- \ 3 \cdot 5 \ 9$	$8 \cdot 3 \ 7$ $- \ 5 \cdot 4 \ 3$	$5 \cdot 2 \ 2$ $- \ 2 \cdot 6 \ 6$	$6 \cdot 1 \ 6$ $- \ 4 \cdot 7 \ 5$
$3 \cdot 3 \ 7$ $- \ 1 \cdot 8 \ 2$	$4 \cdot 4 \ 2$ $- \ 0 \cdot 5 \ 9$	$9 \cdot 3 \ 3$ $- \ 6 \cdot 7 \ 5$	$7 \cdot 1 \ 2$ $- \ 2 \cdot 5 \ 3$
$8 \cdot 4 \ 5$ $- \ 5 \cdot 7 \ 8$	$6 \cdot 3 \ 7$ $- \ 3 \cdot 9 \ 8$	$2 \cdot 1 \ 4$ $- \ 1 \cdot 4 \ 7$	$5 \cdot 0 \ 4$ $- \ 0 \cdot 3 \ 6$

Factor game

56	22	48	50	14	55
16	100	32	24	35	72
54	25	14	42	12	30
10	132	9	40	36	24
18	20	27	64	81	48
33	97	18	45	28	63

Teacher's instructions
A game for two players. Take turns to throw the dice, find the total score and place a counter on a square whose number has the total as a factor. When you place the counter, you must say the pair of factors that multiply together to make the number. You cannot place a counter on a number that is already covered. Check each other's moves. The winner is the first to have four counters in any straight line.

Materials
2 dice
A set of counters each

Name _____

Factor table

Complete the factor table.

Which columns have lots of entries?

Factors

Numbers	1	2	3	4	5	6	7	8	9	10	11	12	13	14	15	16	17	18	19	20
1	1																			
2	1	2																		
3	1		3																	
4	1	2		4																
5	1				5															
6	1	2	3			6														
7																				
8																				
9																				
10																				
11																				
12																				
13																				
14																				
15																				
16																				
17																				
18																				
19																				
20																				

60

Name _____

Prime numbers

Colour the number 1 square.
Colour all the multiples of 2 except 2.
Colour all the multiples of 3 except 3.
Colour all the multiples of 5 except 5.
Colour all the multiples of 7 except 7.

What do you notice about the numbers left uncoloured?

1	2	3	4	5	6	7	8	9	10
11	12	13	14	15	16	17	18	19	20
21	22	23	24	25	26	27	28	29	30
31	32	33	34	35	36	37	38	39	40
41	42	43	44	45	46	47	48	49	50
51	52	53	54	55	56	57	58	59	60
61	62	63	64	65	66	67	68	69	70
71	72	73	74	75	76	77	78	79	80
81	82	83	84	85	86	87	88	89	90
91	92	93	94	95	96	97	98	99	100

Name _____

Sets of prime numbers

| 1 | 2 | 3 | 4 | 5 | 6 | 7 | 8 | 9 |

Make sets of prime numbers.
They can be 1-digit or 2-digit prime numbers.

**Number cards
(1 to 9)**

Here is one set:

| 5 | 7 | 3 1 | 2 9 |

The cards | 6 | and | 8 | have not been used.

Here is another set:

| 2 | 5 | 3 7 | 6 1 |

The cards | 4 | and | 8 | have not been used.

Make several
different sets.   How many cards
can you use in a set?

Name _____

The I to I6 puzzle

Write the numbers I to I6, one in each box, so that all the numbers match both the row heading and the column heading.

Draw a large grid on paper, make small cards from I to I6, then experiment to solve the puzzle.

	numbers less than 7	numbers between II and I7	numbers less than I2	factors of 36
odd numbers				
even numbers				
multiples of 2				
prime numbers				

Name _____

Positives and negatives

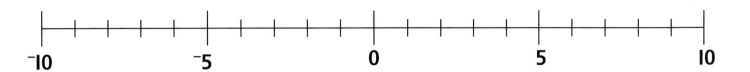

$^-10$ $^-5$ 0   5   10

Write the difference between each pair of numbers.

1. 4 and 2   d =

2. 5 and 10   d =

3. 0 and 7   d =

4. $^-3$ and 0   d =

5. $^-5$ and $^-2$ d =

6. $^-7$ and 1   d =

7. 2 and $^-3$ d =

8. 3 and 6   d =

9. $^-1$ and $^-9$ d =

10. $^-8$ and 4   d =

11. $^-10$ and 10   d =

12. 6 and $^-1$ d =

13. $^-5$ and 1   d =

14. $^-3$ and $^-8$ d =

15. 4 and 7   d =

16. $^-4$ and 7   d =

17. $^-7$ and 4   d =

18. $^-7$ and $^-4$ d =

Name _____

Difference tables

Complete these difference tables.

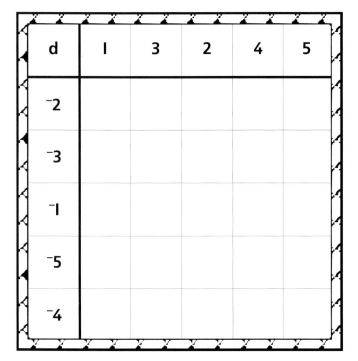

d	1	3	2	4	5
-2					
-3					
-1					
-5					
-4					

d	1	-3	2	-4	0
3					
-1					
2					
-2					
5					

d	-5	5	-6	7	-8
3					
-4					
2					
-7					
6					

d	-10	0	4	-2	7
-5					
3					
-1					
9					
-3					

Name _____

Estimating, then multiplying

Circle the answer which you estimate to be the nearest, then multiply the two numbers together.

Check with a calculator and write down the nearest estimate of the three.

Multiplication	Estimates	My multiplication	Calculator multiplication	Nearest estimate
29 × 20	500 600 700			
33 × 30	1000 1500 2000			
41 × 20	800 900 1000			
20 × 61	1000 1200 1400			
25 × 21	500 600 700			
15 × 39	200 400 600			
49 × 30	1000 1500 2000			
22 × 19	400 500 600			
51 × 71	1250 2500 3750			
79 × 33	2000 2500 3000			

Name _____

Dice multiplying

Roll a dice to find the multiplying number each time.

If you roll a 'I', then roll again.

A dice

 $\boxed{5}$ × 4·3 = (20) + (1·5) = _21·5_

I. $\boxed{}$ × 2·7 = (   ) + (   ) = _____

2. $\boxed{}$ × 3·1 = (   ) + (   ) = _____

3. $\boxed{}$ × 8·4 = (   ) + (   ) = _____

4. $\boxed{}$ × 7·3 = (   ) + (   ) = _____

5. $\boxed{}$ × 4·9 = (   ) + (   ) = _____

6. $\boxed{}$ × 5·8 = (   ) + (   ) = _____

7. $\boxed{}$ × 9·2 = (   ) + (   ) = _____

8. $\boxed{}$ × 6·6 = (   ) + (   ) = _____

9. $\boxed{}$ × 3·7 = (   ) + (   ) = _____

10. $\boxed{}$ × 9·9 = (   ) + (   ) = _____

Name _____

Target multiplication

Target	Multiplication	Product	Score (difference)
24	☐ × ☐ · ☐☐ =		
30	☐ × ☐ · ☐☐ =		
18	☐ × ☐ · ☐☐ =		
38	☐ × ☐ · ☐☐ =		
9·5	☐ × ☐ · ☐☐ =		
12	☐ × ☐ · ☐☐ =		
51	☐ × ☐ · ☐☐ =		
29	☐ × ☐ · ☐☐ =		
		Total score	

Teacher's instructions
Shuffle the cards and deal out four.
Arrange them to make a multiplication of a 2-place decimal number and
a 1-digit number. Try to get as close as you can to the target.
Score the difference.
Replace the cards, reshuffle them, and repeat for the next target.

Materials
Number cards (1 to 9)

Name _____

Multiplying decimals

Estimate, then multiply.

1. ⬭

$4 \times 1\cdot7$

$4 \times 1\cdot0 \ =$

$4 \times 0\cdot7 \ =$

$4 \times 1\cdot7 \ =$

2. ⬭

$5 \times 2\cdot8$

$5 \times 2\cdot0 \ =$

$5 \times 0\cdot8 \ =$

$5 \times 2\cdot8 \ =$

3. ⬭

$6 \times 3\cdot9$

$6 \times 3\cdot0 \ =$

$6 \times 0\cdot9 \ =$

$6 \times 3\cdot9 \ =$

4. ⬭

$3 \times 4\cdot53$

$3 \times 4\cdot0 \ =$

$3 \times 0\cdot5 \ =$

$3 \times 0\cdot03 \ =$

$3 \times 4\cdot53 \ =$

5. ⬭

$7 \times 1\cdot62$

$7 \times 1\cdot0 \ =$

$7 \times 0\cdot6 \ =$

$3 \times 0\cdot02 \ =$

$7 \times 1\cdot62 \ =$

6. ⬭

$5 \times 2\cdot84$

$5 \times 2\cdot0 \ =$

$5 \times 0\cdot8 \ =$

$5 \times 0\cdot04 \ =$

$5 \times 2\cdot84 \ =$

7. ⬭

$4 \times 7\cdot36$

$4 \times \qquad =$

$4 \times \qquad =$

$4 \times \qquad =$

$4 \times \qquad =$

8. ⬭

$6 \times 2\cdot81$

$6 \times \qquad =$

$6 \times \qquad =$

$6 \times \qquad =$

$6 \times \qquad =$

9. ⬭

$8 \times 5\cdot74$

$8 \times \qquad =$

$8 \times \qquad =$

$8 \times \qquad =$

$8 \times \qquad =$

69

Name _____

Dividing

Estimate, then divide.

I. $\boxed{}$

$17\overline{)4\ 2\ 5}$

2. $\boxed{}$

$13\overline{)2\ 3\ 4}$

3. $\boxed{}$

$19\overline{)6\ 0\ 8}$

4. $\boxed{}$

$16\overline{)6\ 8\ 8}$

5. $\boxed{}$

$24\overline{)6\ 7\ 2}$

6. $\boxed{}$

$27\overline{)4\ 3\ 2}$

7. $\boxed{}$

$29\overline{)6\ 9\ 6}$

8. $\boxed{}$

$36\overline{)6\ 1\ 2}$

q. $\boxed{}$

$48\overline{)6\ 2\ 4}$

Name _____

Football attendances

These figures show the number of people attending football matches last Saturday.

Find the average (the mean) attendance for each division.

Premier league

19 000
38 000
55 000
37 000
22 000
15 000
16 000

Average [   ]

Division 1

16 000
15 000
9000
10 000
30 000
15 000
9000

Average [   ]

Division 2

6000
9000
4000
9000
6000
5000
7000
8000
3000

Average [   ]

Division 3

3300
3200
4500
5800
4600
3400
2300
4200
6300
2200

Average [   ]

Name _____

Division trick

Write any 3-digit number.

Repeat the digits to make a 6-digit number.

356   **356356**

Divide it by 11.

Check that the answer is exactly 32 396.

11)356356

Divide this answer by 7.

Check that the answer is exactly 4628.

7)32396

Divide this answer by 13.

Check that the answer is exactly 356.

13)4628

Repeat for different 3-digit numbers.

What do you notice?

Why does the trick work?

First work out
7 × 11 × 13.

Name _____

Dividing decimals

Complete these.

1. ( )

$2 \overline{) 8 \cdot 4}$

2. ( )

$3 \overline{) 9 \cdot 6}$

3. ( )

$4 \overline{) 8 \cdot 8}$

4. ( )

$2 \overline{) 5 \cdot 6}$

5. ( )

$5 \overline{) 9 \cdot 5}$

6. ( )

$6 \overline{) 12 \cdot 6}$

7. ( )

$4 \overline{) 14 \cdot 4}$

8. ( )

$5 \overline{) 16 \cdot 5}$

9. ( )

$7 \overline{) 23 \cdot 8}$

10. ( )

$3 \overline{) 18 \cdot 9}$

11. ( )

$2 \overline{) 27 \cdot 4}$

12. ( )

$8 \overline{) 51 \cdot 2}$

13. ( )

$6 \overline{) 55 \cdot 8}$

14. ( )

$7 \overline{) 43 \cdot 4}$

15. ( )

$9 \overline{) 87 \cdot 3}$

Name _____

Dividing decimals

Write the missing digits.

1.

$$2 \cdot 4$$

$$2 \overline{) \bigcirc \cdot \bigcirc}$$

2.

$$1 \cdot 4$$

$$4 \overline{) \bigcirc \cdot \bigcirc}$$

3.

$$3 \cdot 8$$

$$2 \overline{) \bigcirc \cdot \bigcirc}$$

4.

$$1 \cdot 9$$

$$\bigcirc \overline{) 9 \cdot 5}$$

5.

$$1 \cdot 4$$

$$6 \overline{) \bigcirc \cdot \bigcirc}$$

6.

$$0 \cdot 5$$

$$7 \overline{) \bigcirc \cdot \bigcirc}$$

7.

$$0 \cdot 7$$

$$\bigcirc \overline{) 7 \cdot 0}$$

8.

$$0 \cdot 8$$

$$\bigcirc \overline{) 6 \cdot 4}$$

9.

$$1 \cdot 1$$

$$9 \overline{) \bigcirc \cdot \bigcirc}$$

10.

$$1 \cdot 2$$

$$7 \overline{) \bigcirc \cdot \bigcirc}$$

11.

$$1 \cdot 7$$

$$5 \overline{) \bigcirc \cdot \bigcirc}$$

12.

$$1 \cdot 9$$

$$\bigcirc \overline{) 7 \cdot 6}$$

13.

$$1 \cdot 4$$

$$\bigcirc \overline{) 8 \cdot 4}$$

14.

$$2 \cdot 3$$

$$3 \overline{) \bigcirc \cdot \bigcirc}$$

15.

$$1 \cdot 2$$

$$8 \overline{) \bigcirc \cdot \bigcirc}$$

Name _____

Percentages

> Write what percentage of each grid is shaded.

1.

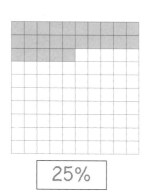

25%

2.

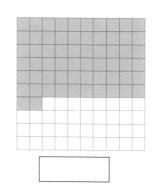

3.

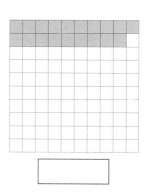

4.

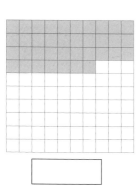

5.

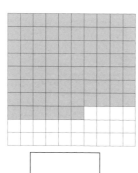

6.

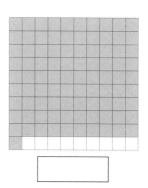

> Colour each grid to match the percentages.

7.

40%

8.

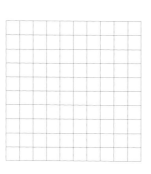

75%

9.

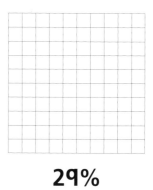

29%

10.

55%

11.

83%

12.

27%

75

Name _____

Percentages

These are the results of 25 football matches.

4–1	2–1	3–4	3–5	3–0
1–3	0–0	1–4	2–4	1–2
2–2	3–1	4–2	1–3	3–1
5–1	2–2	3–2	1–1	4–2
0–1	1–1	2–4	2–0	3–3

Write these percentages.

1. teams scoring 0 goals ⬭ 10 %   **2.** teams scoring 1 goal ⬭ %

3. teams scoring 2 goals ⬭ %   **4.** teams scoring 3 goals ⬭ %

5. teams scoring 4 goals ⬭ %   **6.** teams scoring 5 goals ⬭ %

7. teams scoring more than 2 goals ⬭ %

8. teams scoring fewer than 2 goals ⬭ %

9. drawn matches ⬭ %

10. matches with fewer than 4 goals ⬭ %

11. matches with more than 5 goals ⬭ %

Percentages

(Complete these.)

**50%
OFF !**

1.   10% of £20 = _____

2.   20% of £50 = _____

3.   50% of £40 = _____

4.   100% of £60 = _____

5.   30% of £30 = _____

6.   40% of £100 = _____

7.   25% of £80 = _____

8.   75% of £4 = _____

9.   80% of £50 = _____

10.   10% of £25 = _____

11.   30% of £100 = _____

12.   60% of £10 = _____

13.   50% of £20 = _____

14.   20% of £20 = _____

15.   90% of £10 = _____

16.   60% of £5 = _____

17.   30% of £40 = _____

18.   5% of £20 = _____

19.   50% of £120 = _____

20.   75% of £80 = _____

Abacus Ginn and Company 2001. Copying permitted for purchasing school only. This material is not copyright free.

Name _____

Fractions and decimals

Use number cards 0 to 9.

Find different ways of placing 4 cards to make an equivalent fraction and decimal.

•

‖

Fractions and percentages

Write each fraction as a percentage.

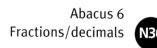

1. $\dfrac{1}{10}$ = ☐ %

2. $\dfrac{1}{100}$ = ☐ %

3. $\dfrac{1}{20}$ = ☐ %

4. $\dfrac{1}{2}$ = ☐ %

5. $\dfrac{1}{4}$ = ☐ %

6. $\dfrac{1}{5}$ = ☐ %

7. $\dfrac{3}{10}$ = ☐ %

8. $\dfrac{3}{4}$ = ☐ %

9. $\dfrac{2}{5}$ = ☐ %

10. $\dfrac{1}{50}$ = ☐ %

11. $\dfrac{11}{20}$ = ☐ %

12. $\dfrac{1}{25}$ = ☐ %

13. $\dfrac{9}{10}$ = ☐ %

14. $\dfrac{4}{5}$ = ☐ %

15. $\dfrac{17}{50}$ = ☐ %

16. $\dfrac{7}{10}$ = ☐ %

17. $\dfrac{6}{10}$ = ☐ %

18. $\dfrac{2}{50}$ = ☐ %

19. $\dfrac{6}{25}$ = ☐ %

20. $\dfrac{3}{5}$ = ☐ %

Name _____

Fractions, percentages and decimals

Write <, > or = between each pair.

1. $\frac{16}{100}$ ⬡ 60%

2. 30% ⬡ 0·3

3. 0·4 ⬡ $\frac{4}{100}$

4. $\frac{1}{4}$ ⬡ 40%

5. 50% ⬡ $\frac{5}{10}$

6. $\frac{7}{10}$ ⬡ 0·72

7. 0·55 ⬡ $\frac{1}{2}$

8. 60% ⬡ $\frac{6}{10}$

9. $\frac{5}{10}$ ⬡ 25%

10. $\frac{4}{5}$ ⬡ 0·8

11. 40% ⬡ $\frac{4}{5}$

12. $\frac{18}{100}$ ⬡ 80%

13. $\frac{9}{10}$ ⬡ 0·91

14. 70% ⬡ $\frac{70}{100}$

15. 0·64 ⬡ 65%

16. $\frac{8}{10}$ ⬡ 75%

17. $\frac{1}{10}$ ⬡ 0·1

18. 1·2 ⬡ $\frac{5}{10}$

19. 80% ⬡ $\frac{8}{100}$

20. 1·0 ⬡ 100%

Name _____

Proportion

Write the proportion of holes containing pegs.

I.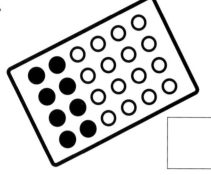

2.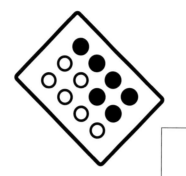

3.

4.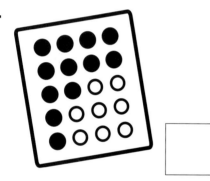

5.

6.

7.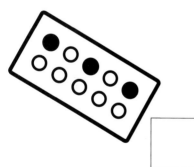

8.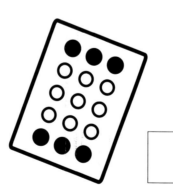

q.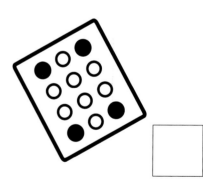

10.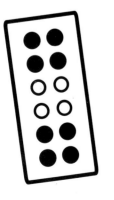

II.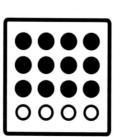

12.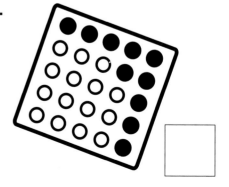

Name _____

Proportion

	Matches			
	Played	Won	Drawn	Lost
Griffins	12	6	3	3
Falcons	10	8	1	1
Tigers	12	4	2	6
Rams	8	2	4	2
Bears	9	6	3	0
Cheetahs	10	2	5	3

Write the proportion of matches that the:

1.	Griffins won	_____
3.	Bears drew	_____
5.	Cheetahs drew	_____
7.	Griffins lost	_____
9.	Falcons won	_____
11.	Bears lost	_____
13.	Tigers lost	_____
15.	Rams lost	_____
17.	Cheetahs lost	_____

2.	Falcons lost	_____
4.	Tigers won	_____
6.	Rams drew	_____
8.	Cheetahs won	_____
10.	Tigers drew	_____
12.	Rams won	_____
14.	Falcons drew	_____
16.	Bears won	_____
18.	Griffins drew	_____

Name _____

Ratio

Write the ratio of the two amounts.

1.

ratio ___4:1___

2.

ratio _____

3.

ratio _____

4.

ratio _____

5.

ratio _____

6.

ratio _____

7.

ratio _____

8.

ratio _____

83

Name _____

Ratio

Shade the grids in these ratios of shaded : non-shaded.

I.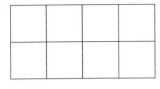

3:I

2.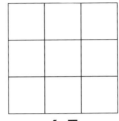

4:5

3.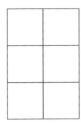

I:2

4.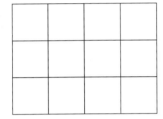

2:I

5.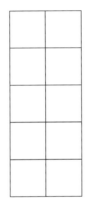

I:I

6.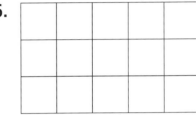

I:4

7.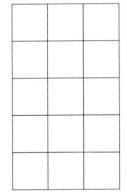

2:3

8.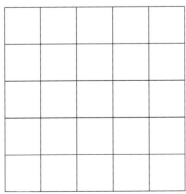

5:7

10.

3:I

q.

3:2

II.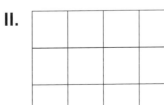

5:I

84

Name _____

Checking calculations

Complete the additions to check each calculation.

I. 114 – 76 = 38   38 + 76   = _____

2. 202 – 59 = 143   143 + 59   = _____

3. 23·9 – 16 = 7·9   16 + 7·9   = _____

4. 42·2 – 19 = 25·2   25·2 + 19   = _____

5. 13·5 – 7·7 = 5·8   5·8 + 7·7   = _____

6. 6·45 – 3·65 = 2·8   2·8 + 3·65 = _____

7. 19·15 – 13·9 = 5·45   5·45 + 13·9 = _____

8. 11·91 – 7·63 = 4·28   _____ + _____ = _____

9. 7·04 – 4·96 = 2·08   _____ + _____ = _____

10. 17·37 – 7·7 = 9·67   _____ + _____ = _____

Using arithmetical facts

Find the missing digits.

1. $2 \cdot \underline{\hspace{1cm}} + \underline{\hspace{1cm}} \cdot 6 = 10 \cdot 0$

2. $\underline{\hspace{1cm}} \cdot 8 + 3 \cdot 7 \underline{\hspace{1cm}} = 9 \cdot \underline{\hspace{1cm}} 2$

3. $\underline{\hspace{1cm}} \cdot 43 + 5 \cdot \underline{\hspace{1cm}} 8 = 12 \cdot 2 \underline{\hspace{1cm}}$

4. $5 \cdot \underline{\hspace{1cm}} 4 + 6 \cdot 0 \underline{\hspace{1cm}} = 1 \underline{\hspace{1cm}} \cdot 43$

5. $8 \cdot 6 \underline{\hspace{1cm}} - 2 \cdot \underline{\hspace{1cm}} 1 = \underline{\hspace{1cm}} \cdot 92$

6. $\underline{\hspace{1cm}} \cdot 6 - 3 \cdot \underline{\hspace{1cm}} = 5 \cdot 9$

7. $12 \cdot 3 - \underline{\hspace{1cm}} \cdot \underline{\hspace{1cm}} 6 = 8 \cdot 1 \underline{\hspace{1cm}}$

8. $7 \cdot 5 \underline{\hspace{1cm}} - \underline{\hspace{1cm}} \cdot 9 = 5 \cdot \underline{\hspace{1cm}} 2$

9. $\underline{\hspace{1cm}} \cdot 31 - 0 \cdot 7 \underline{\hspace{1cm}} = 7 \cdot \underline{\hspace{1cm}} 3$

10. $9 - 4 \cdot \underline{\hspace{1cm}} 8 = \underline{\hspace{1cm}} \cdot 6 \underline{\hspace{1cm}}$

86

Name _____

Squares and square roots

Complete these.

squares			square roots		
1×1	=	1	$\sqrt{1}$	=	1
2×2	=	4	$\sqrt{4}$	=	2
3×3	=	9	$\sqrt{9}$	=	3
4×4	=	___	___	=	4
5×5	=	___	___	=	5
6×6	=	___	___	=	6
7×7	=	___	___	=	7
8×8	=	___	___	=	8
9×9	=	___	___	=	9
10×10	=	___	___	=	10
11×11	=	___	___	=	11
12×12	=	___	___	=	12
20×20	=	___	___	=	20
30×30	=	___	___	=	30
40×40	=	___	___	=	40

3^2

9

87

Name _____

Squares

Use multiplying to complete these.

$$15^2 = 225$$

$$25^2 = 625$$

$$35^2 = 1225$$

$$45^2 = \underline{\hspace{2cm}}$$

$$55^2 = \underline{\hspace{2cm}}$$

$$65^2 = \underline{\hspace{2cm}}$$

$$75^2 = \underline{\hspace{2cm}}$$

$$85^2 = \underline{\hspace{2cm}}$$

$$95^2 = \underline{\hspace{2cm}}$$

Write about the pattern you notice.

Can you find a quick way of squaring a 2-digit number with a units digit of 5?

Name _____

Square root estimating

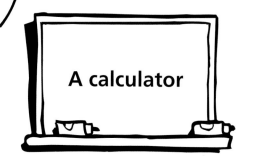

> Estimate the square root of each number.
> Use a calculator to check it accurately.

> Score the difference between the two.

> Find your total score.

A calculator

Square root	Estimated answer	Accurate answer	Difference
$\sqrt{64}$			
$\sqrt{121}$			
$\sqrt{400}$			
$\sqrt{900}$			
$\sqrt{1225}$			
$\sqrt{2916}$			
$\sqrt{3249}$			
$\sqrt{5329}$			
$\sqrt{729}$			
$\sqrt{3136}$			
		Total difference	

Name _____

Pascal's triangle

Look at this triangular pattern of numbers.
Complete the next three lines.

Investigate and describe any patterns you see.

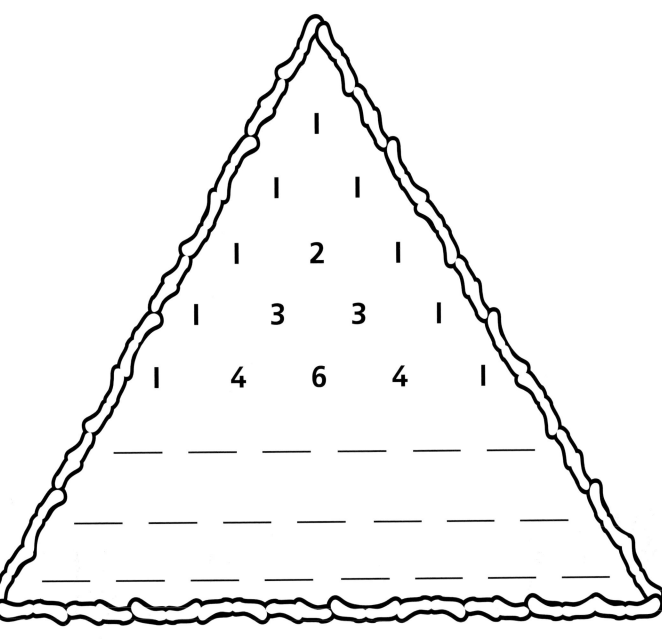

Name _____

Digit patterns

Choose any three digits.

Use them to make all the 2-digit numbers you can.

Add them together.

```
  47
  41
  74
  71
  14
  17
―――
 264
```

Divide this number by the total of the three digits you chose.

$$264 \div 12 = 22$$

Repeat using three different digits.
What do you notice?

Try this using the digits to make 3-digit numbers.

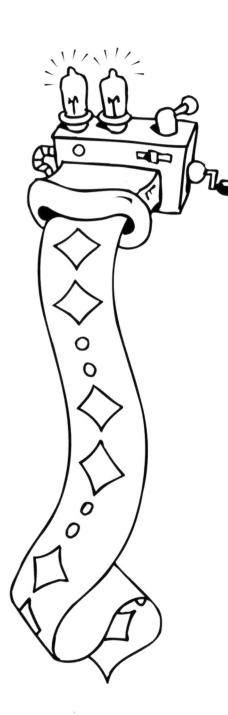

Abacus Ginn and Company 2001. Copying permitted for purchasing school only. This material is not copyright free.

Name _____

Odds and evens

'O' is odd, 'E' is even.

Write 'O' or 'E' for each answer.

1. $O + E =$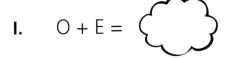

2. $E - O =$

3. $O \times O =$

4. $E \times E =$

5. $O \times E =$

6. $O \times E \times O =$

7. $E \times E \times O =$

8. $O \times (E + O) =$

9. $E \times (O + O) =$

10. $(O - E) \times O =$

11. $(O - O) \times E =$

12. $(O + E) \times (E - O) =$

13. $(E - E) \times (O - O) =$

14. $(E + O) \times (E - O) =$

15. $(O - E) \times (E - O) =$

16. $(O \times E) + (E \times E) =$

Name _____

Inches and centimetres

Find some objects which are less than one metre long.

Estimate the lengths of each in centimetres and in inches. Write them in the table.

Measure the lengths accurately in centimetres and inches. How close are your estimates?

A ruler

object	estimate (cm)	length (cm)	estimate (inches)	length (inches)

Name _____

Yards, feet, inches, metres, centimetres

> Write <, > or = between each pair.

1. 3 feet  I yard

2. 10 inches  $\frac{1}{2}$ foot

3. 8 feet 3 yards

4. $1\frac{1}{2}$ yards 4 feet

5. 40 inches $1\frac{1}{2}$ yards

6. $2\frac{1}{2}$ feet 32 inches

7. $\frac{1}{2}$ yard 20 inches

8. $5\frac{1}{2}$ feet 2 yards

9. 120 inches  3 yards

10. 4 feet  50 inches

11. 12 inches I foot

12. 30 inches  $2\frac{1}{2}$ feet

13. 4 metres 12 feet

14. 6 inches  18 cm

15. 50 cm 2 feet

16. $1\frac{1}{2}$ yards 110 cm

Name _____

Pounds, ounces, grams, kilograms

Write <, > or = between each pair.

1.　2 lb 1 kg

2.　400 g 1 lb

3.　30 oz 1 kg

4.　2 lb 30 oz

5.　1000g 1 kg

6.　$\frac{1}{4}$ lb 6 oz

7.　$\frac{1}{2}$ kg 1 lb

8.　9 oz $\frac{1}{2}$ lb

9.　200 g 10 oz

10.　750 g $1\frac{1}{2}$ lb

11.　$\frac{1}{4}$ kg 10 oz

12.　$\frac{1}{2}$ lb 300 g

13.　45 oz 3 lb 2 oz

14.　600 g 1 lb 8 oz

15.　4 kg 10 lb

16.　$2\frac{1}{2}$ kg 72 oz

Name _____

Pints, gallons, litres, centilitres, millilitres

Complete these.

1. I gallon = ⬡ pints

2. 12 pints = ⬡ gallons

3. I l = ⬡ ml

4. I l = ⬡ cl

5. I cl = ⬡ ml

6. 500 ml = ⬡ l

7. 300 ml = ⬡ cl

8. $\frac{1}{2}$ l = ⬡ cl

9. $2\frac{1}{2}$ gallons = ⬡ pints

10. I l ≈ ⬡ pints

11. I gallon ≈ ⬡ l

12. 45 cl = ⬡ ml

13. 4 l ≈ ⬡ pints

14. 9l ≈ ⬡ gallons

15. 1·3 l = ⬡ cl

16. 4·5cl = ⬡ ml

17. 5·3 l = ⬡ ml

18. 150 ml = ⬡ l

Name _____

Area of a rectangle

Imagine rectangles that have one corner in the top left square of the grid.

Write the area in the bottom right square of the grid.

Complete the grid, writing a number in each square. What do you notice about the completed grid?

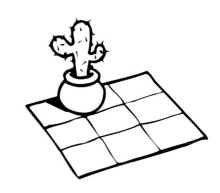

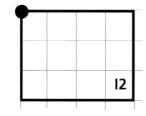

12

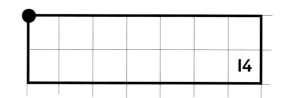

14

14

12

10

Name _____

Surface area

Write the surface area of these cubes and cuboids.

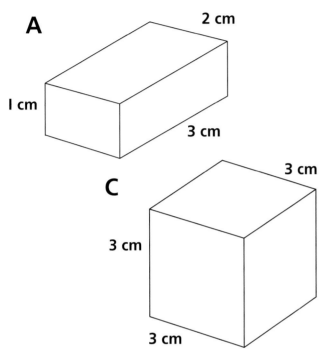

A
2 cm
1 cm
3 cm

C
3 cm
3 cm
3 cm
3 cm

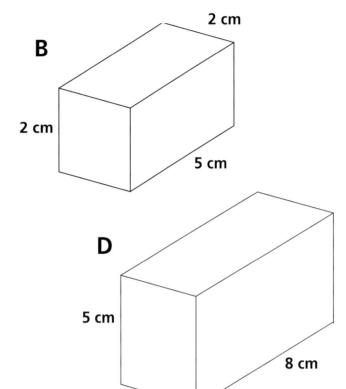

B
2 cm
2 cm
5 cm

D
5 cm
8 cm
4 cm

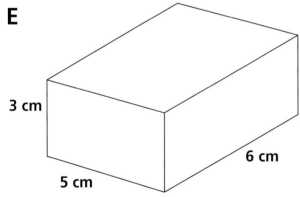

E
3 cm
6 cm
5 cm

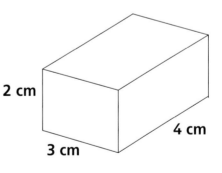

F
2 cm
4 cm
3 cm

Cuboid	Area of top	Area of side	Area of front	Total surface area
A				
B				
C				
D				
E				
F				

Name _____

Area of a right-angled triangle

Measure the sides, then find the area of each triangle.

1.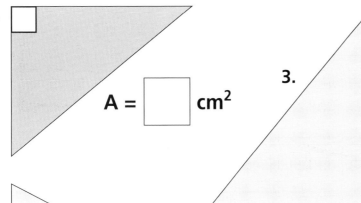

A = ☐ cm²

2.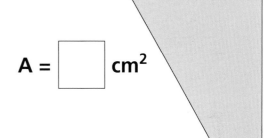

A = ☐ cm²

3.

A = ☐ cm²

4.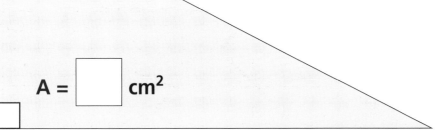

A = ☐ cm²

5.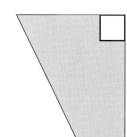

A = ☐ cm²

6.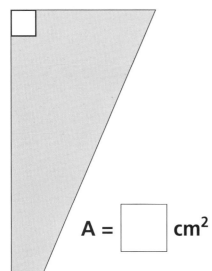

A = ☐ cm²

7.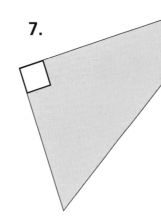

A = ☐ cm²

8.

A = ☐ cm²

99

Name _____

Area

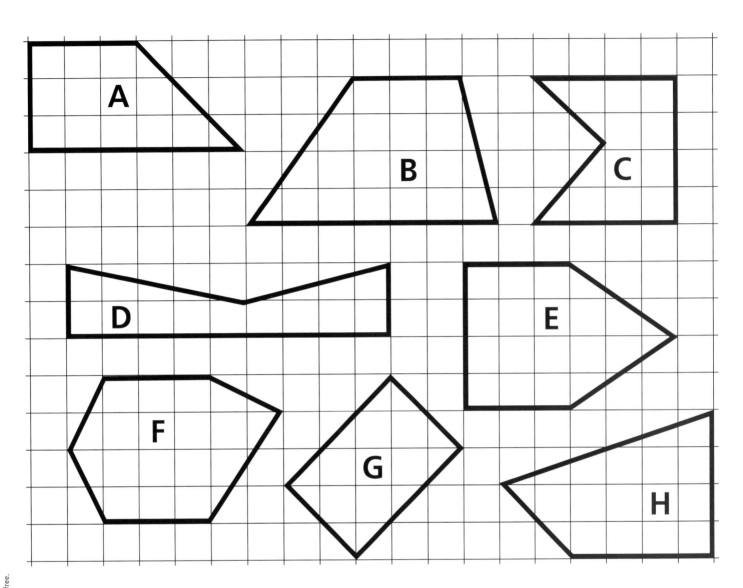

Estimate the area of each shape. Put the shapes in order, smallest area to largest area. Write the letters.

smallest   largest

Measure the areas, and then write the correct order here.

smallest   largest

How good was your estimated order?

Name _____

Perimeter

Estimate the perimeter of each shape in centimeters.

Measure the length of each side and record it in centimetres, using decimal notation.

Find the perimeters accurately.

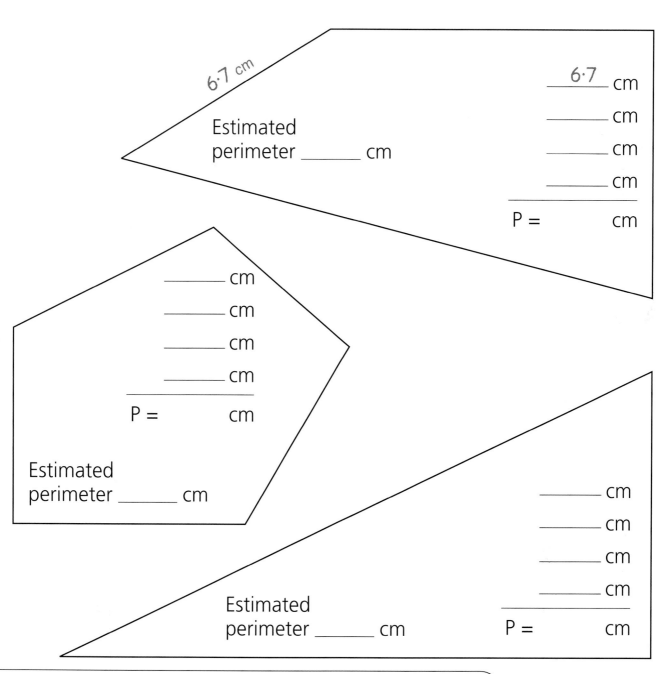

6·7 cm

Estimated
perimeter _____ cm

_____6·7___ cm
_____ cm
_____ cm
_____ cm
P = _____ cm

_____ cm
_____ cm
_____ cm
_____ cm
P = _____ cm

Estimated
perimeter _____ cm

Estimated
perimeter _____ cm

_____ cm
_____ cm
_____ cm
_____ cm
P = _____ cm

Draw three of your own shapes and measure their perimeters.

Name _____

Angles at a point

Write the missing angles.

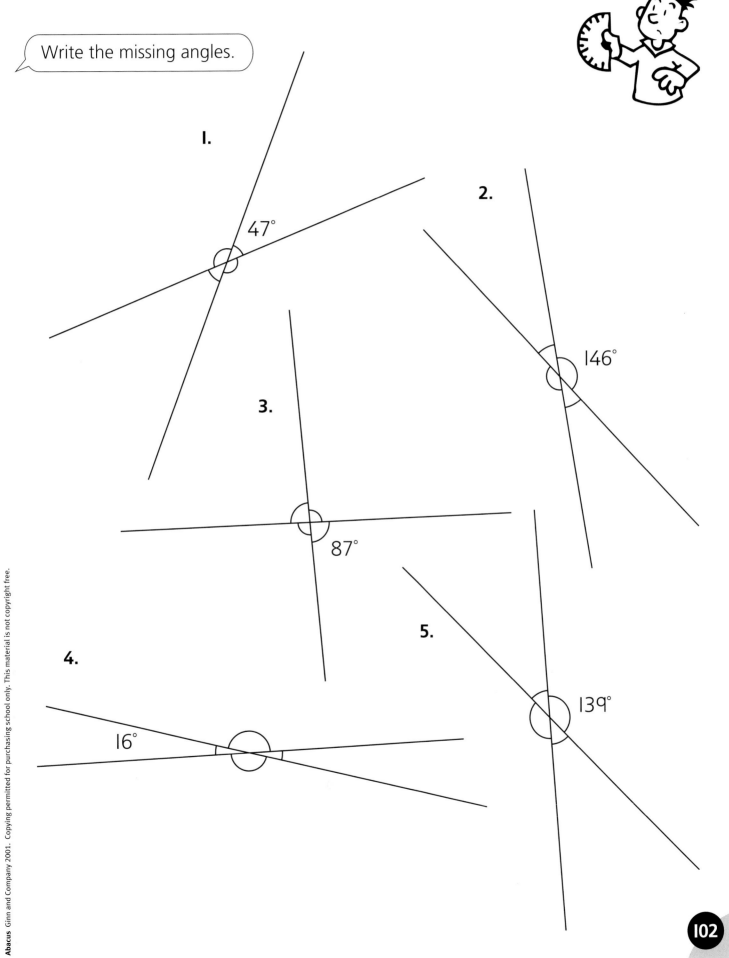

1.

47°

2.

146°

3.

87°

4.

16°

5.

139°

Name _____

Angles of a triangle

Write the missing angles.

I.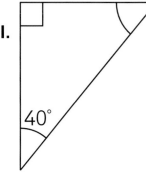
40°

2.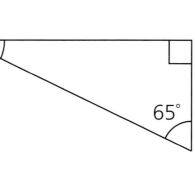
65°

3.
72°

4. 62° 60°

5. 97°
45°

6.
28° 115°

7. 31°
82°

8. 128°
41°

q. 37°

10. 35° 54°

Name _____

Angles in polygons

The three angles of a triangle total 2 right angles (or 180°).

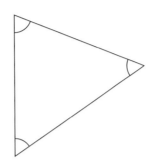

Find the total of the angles of a pentagon by splitting it into 3 triangles.

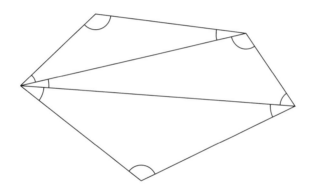

Find the total of the angles of polygons with different numbers of sides.

Draw a table to record the results.

Number of sides of polygon/name	Angle total	
	right angles	degrees
3, triangle	2	180°
4, quadrilateral		
5, pentagon		
6, hexagon		

Name _____

Coordinates

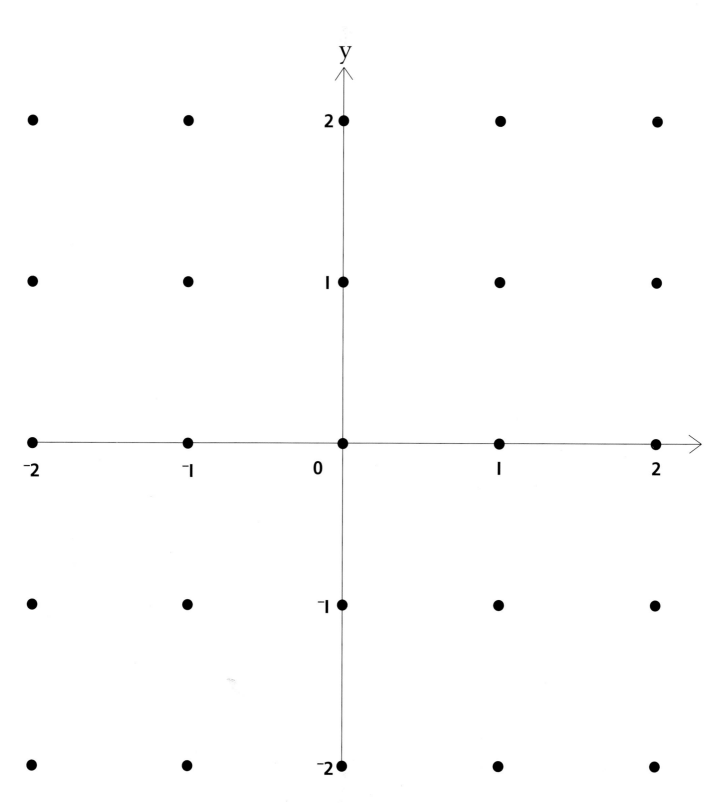

Teacher's instructions
A game for two players. The red dice shows the horizontal (x) coordinate, and the black dice shows the vertical (y) coordinate. Take turns to throw both dice, and place one of your counters on the matching point. If you throw a blank, you can choose a coordinate. You cannot place a counter on a point that is already covered. The winner is the first to have three counters in any straight line.

Materials
2 dice (made by writing on blank cubes, each with one blank face and ⁻2, ⁻1, 0, 1, 2 written on the other faces; one dice is written in red, and one in black.)
A set of counters each

Name _____

Road signs

Write which of these road signs have line symmetry.

1. 	**2.** 	**3.** 
4. 	**5.** 	**6.** 
7. 	**8.** 	**9.** 
10. 	**11.** 	**12.** 

Find out what each sign means.

Use the *Highway Code* to draw and cut out some more road signs.
Sort them into symmetrical and non-symmetrical shapes.

Name _____

Reflections

Each pair of points are reflections of each other in one or both of the axes.

Write either 'x-axis', 'y-axis', or 'x- and y-axis' for each.

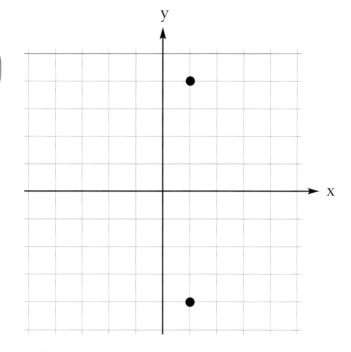

I.   (1, 4) and (1, ⁻4)   x-axis
_____

2.   (3, ⁻2) and (⁻3, ⁻2)
_____

3.   (⁻1, 5) and (1, 5)
_____

4.   (2, ⁻3) and (2, 3)
_____

5.   (⁻4, ⁻3) and (4, ⁻3)
_____

6.   (1, 3) and (⁻1, ⁻3)
_____

7.   (4, 6) and (⁻4, 6)
_____

8.   (0, 3) and (0, ⁻3)
_____

9.   (5, 0) and (⁻5, 0)
_____

10.   (9, ⁻4) and (⁻9, 4)
_____

Name _____

Translations

> Write the coordinates of the vertex A after these translations of the shape.

I. up 2, left 3   (,   )

2. down 4, left I   (,   )

3. right I, down 5   (,   )

4. up 6, right 2   (,   )

5. left 4, up 4, right I   (,   )

6. right 2, down 7, left I0 (,   )

7. up 5, left 6, down 9   (,   )

8. left 4, up 3, right 6, down 2 (,   )

> Describe the translations between these points in two moves.

9. from (3, 5) to (⁻2, 4) _____

I0. from (⁻I, ⁻3) to (I, 4) _____

II. from (3, ⁻2) to (⁻3, 2) _____

I2. from (⁻4, I) to (⁻3, ⁻2) _____

I3. from (5, ⁻I) to (I, ⁻5) _____

I4. from (0, 0) to (⁻4, 3) _____

Name _____

Open cubes

Which of these are nets for an open cube?

Draw them on paper, cut them out and fold them to test.

Write 'yes' or 'no' in the table.

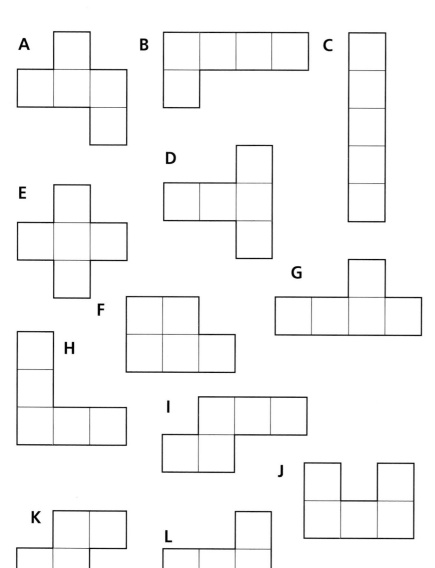

	Open cube?
A	
B	
C	
D	
E	
F	
G	
H	
I	
J	
K	
L	

Colour pairs of parallel faces on each net above.
Use a different colour for each pair in a net.

Name _____

A tetrahedron

Cut out four card rectangles, each 8 cm x 14 cm, putting a tab on one end of each.

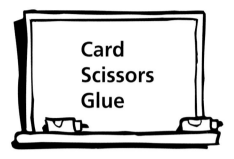

Join them to make a longer rectangle.

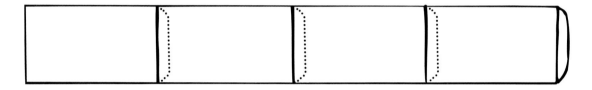

Draw a zig-zag line of diagonals, and score or crease each one.

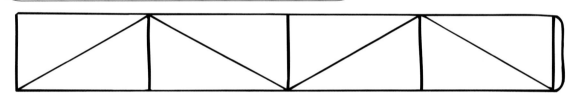

Glue the last tab to make a hollow box.

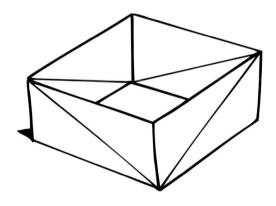

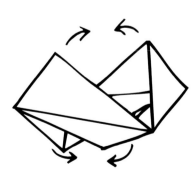

Now fold your shape to make a triangular-based pyramid (a tetrahedron).

Shapes with parallel sides

This shape has
one pair of parallel sides.

This shape has
two pairs of parallel sides.

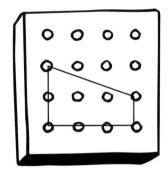
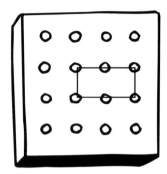

Draw four different shapes, each
with one pair of parallel sides.

Write their names
underneath.

_____   _____   _____   _____

Draw four different shapes, each
with two pairs of parallel sides.

Write their names
underneath.

_____   _____   _____   _____

III

Name _____

Shading shapes

Shade part of each square to make the named shape. All shapes must be different.

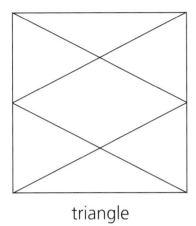
triangle

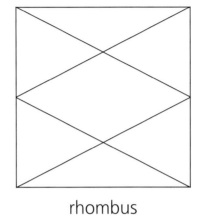
rhombus

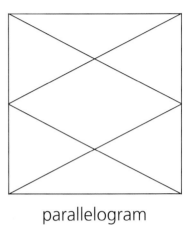
parallelogram

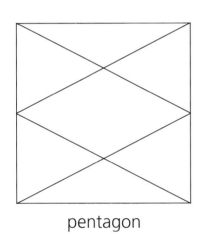
pentagon

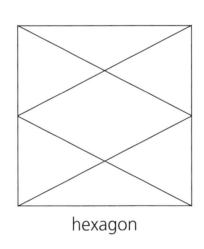
hexagon

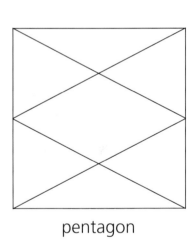
pentagon

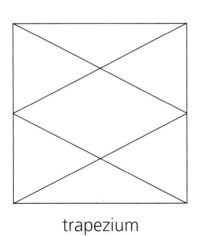
trapezium

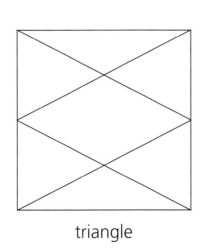
triangle

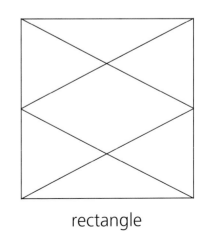
rectangle

Name _____

Naming shapes

Write the name of each shaded shape.

1.
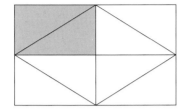
_____

2.
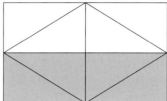
_____

3.
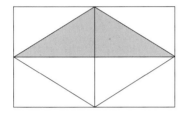
_____

4.
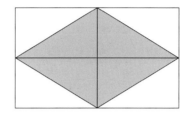
_____

5.
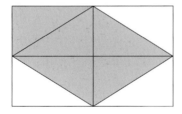
_____

6.
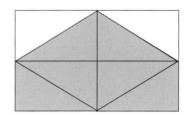
_____

7.
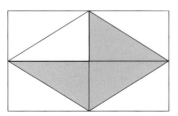
_____

8.
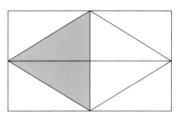
_____

9.
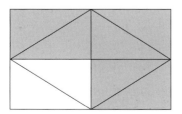
_____

10.
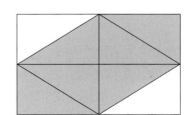
_____

Abacus Ginn and Company 2001. Copying permitted for purchasing school only. This material is not copyright free.

Name _____

Cutting up a rhombus

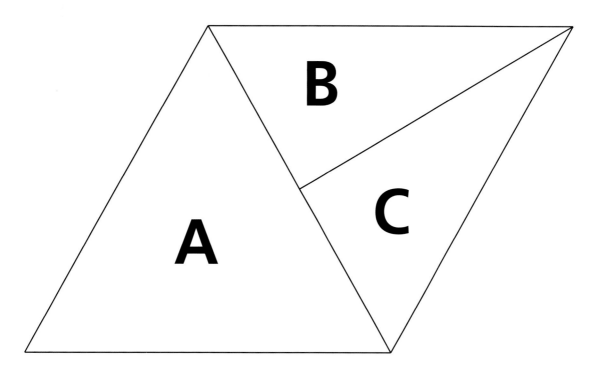

Cut out the three pieces of the rhombus.

Make shapes by joining the pieces along sides of equal length.

Join any two pieces to make these shapes.

a kite

a rectangle

2 different parallelograms

2 different isosceles triangles

Investigate making different shapes using all three pieces.

Name _____

Grouped frequencies

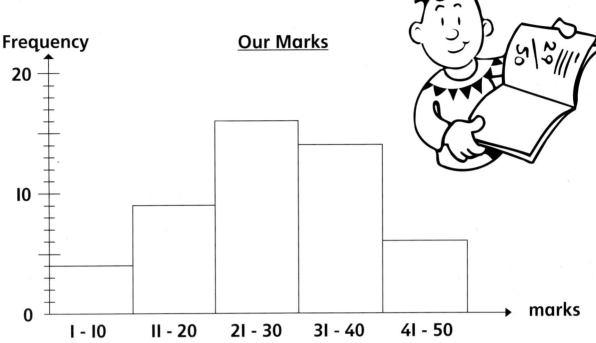

Abacus Ginn and Company 2001. Copying permitted for purchasing school only. This material is not copyright free.

How many children had marks:

I. between 21 and 30? ☐   **2.** between 41 and 50? ☐

3. between 1 and 10? ☐   **4.** between 31 and 40? ☐

5. between 11 and 20? ☐   **6.** 20 or less? ☐

7. more than 30? ☐   **8.** 30 or less? ☐

9. more than 20? ☐   **10.** between 21 and 40? ☐

11. between 1 and 30? ☐

Which group of marks was scored by:

12. 9 children? ☐   **13.** 14 children? ☐

14. 6 children? ☐   **15.** 4 children? ☐

16. 16 children? ☐

How many children took the test?   **17.** ☐

Name _____

Timing

Use a stopwatch showing hundredths of a second.

Start and stop the watch 50 times.
Record the hundredths of a second each time.

Complete the table and draw a graph to show the results.

hundredths of a second	frequency	total
00–09		
10–19		
20–29		
30–39		
40–49		
50–59		
60–69		
70–79		
80–89		
90–99		

Name _____

Pie chart game

A

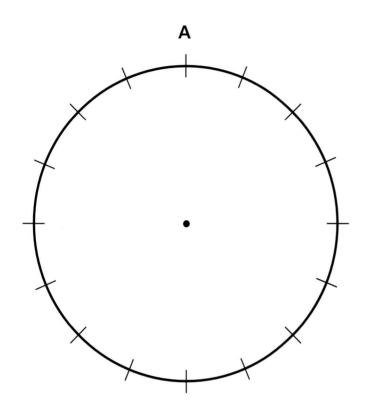

B

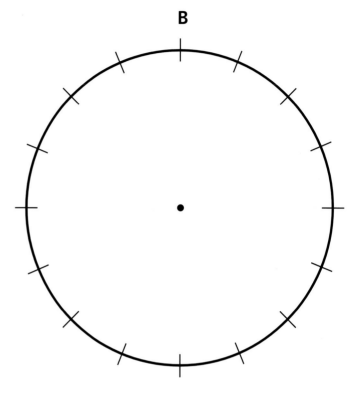

dice throw	tally	total
1		
2		
3		
4		
5		
6		

dice throw	tally	total
1		
2		
3		
4		
5		
6		

Teacher's instructions
A game for two players.
Choose to be A or B. A throws the dice 32 times, and records the scores in the
left-hand table. B throws the dice 16 times, and records the scores in the
right-hand table. Each player then draws a pie chart to show their scores.
Check each other's drawings.
The winner is the player who draws the largest slice.

Materials
A dice

117

Name _____

Favourite pets

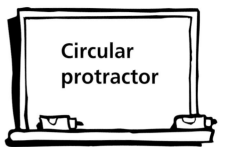

Circular
protractor

Children in a class of 24 have these pets.

Draw a pie chart to show the different types of pet.

Use a circular protractor to divide the
circle into 24 arcs of 15° each.

Draw the slices to match the data.

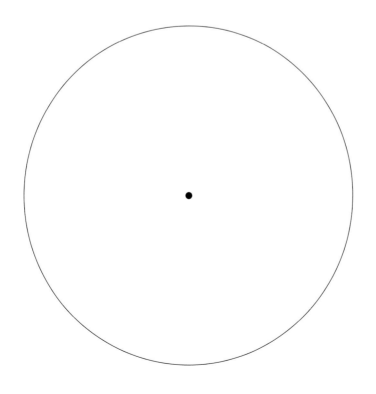

Collect your own data based on pets and draw a pie chart.

118

Name _____

Inches and centimetres

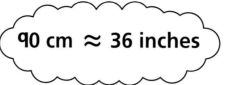

90 cm ≈ 36 inches

Conversion graph for inches and centimetres

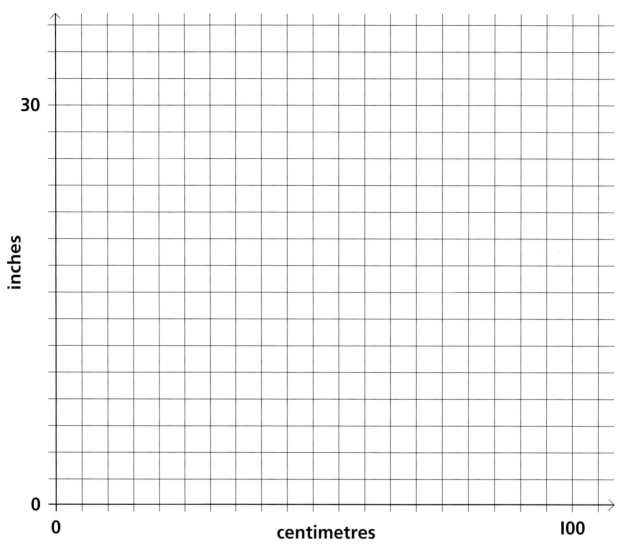

Draw a conversion graph to convert from inches to centimetres.

Label the rest of the axes. Mark the point (90, 36), then draw a conversion line.

Use the graph to write some conversions from centimetres to inches.

I. _____ cm = _____ inches

2. _____ cm = _____ inches

3. _____ cm = _____ inches

4. _____ cm = _____ inches

5. _____ inches = _____ cm

6. _____ inches = _____ cm

Name _____

Averages

Write the mean of the numbers in each row.

mean

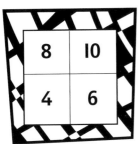

8	10
4	6

_____

_____

mean

3	5
2	8

_____

_____

mean

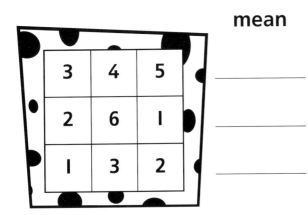

3	4	5
2	6	1
1	3	2

_____

_____

_____

mean

5	4	9
3	6	9
5	4	6

_____

_____

_____

mean

3	2	4	7
2	3	2	5
4	5	6	5
1	0	3	4

_____

_____

_____

_____

mean

3	7	6	8
5	8	9	10
10	5	15	10
4	6	8	10

_____

_____

_____

_____

Name _____

Card averages

Use these number cards.

2 **4** **6** **8** **10**

2 **4** **6** **8** **10**

2 **4** **6** **8** **10**

Find different pairs of cards that have a mean of 2, of 3, of 4 …

2 **6**   mean 4

4 **4**   mean 4

Find sets of three cards that have a mean of 2, of 3, of 4 …

121

Name _____

Probability

These are nets for dice. For each dice, write the probability of throwing these numbers.

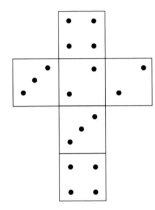

I. 2 _____

2. more than 2 _____

3. 3 _____

4. an even number _____

5. 4 _____

6. an odd number _____

	6	
4	5	7
	5	
	8	

7. 4 _____

8. 5 _____

9. 5 or 6 _____

10. an odd number _____

II. less than 6 _____

12. more than 4 _____

	2	
4	5	4
	3	
	2	

13. 2 _____

14. 3 _____

15. 4 _____

16. less than 5 _____

17. 2 or 3 _____

18. more than 2 _____

Name _____

Tossing coins

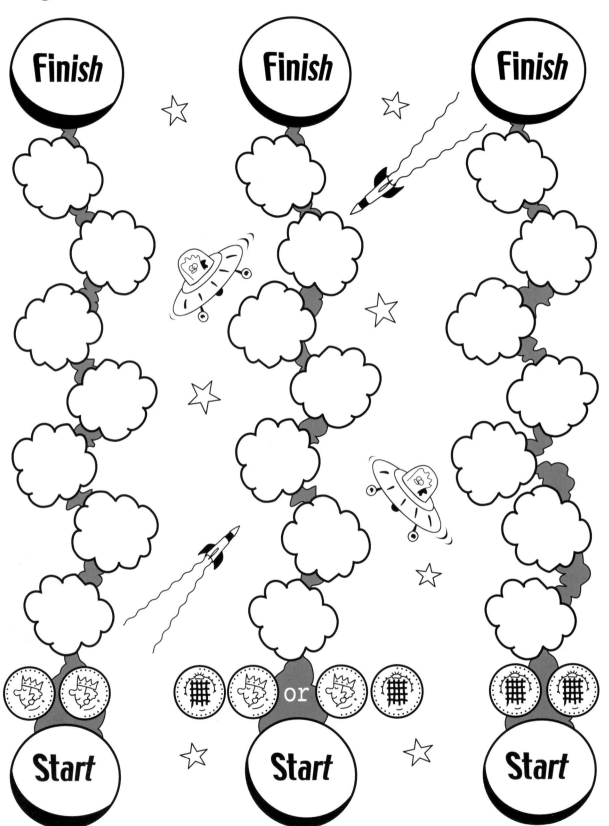

Teacher's instructions
A game for one or two players.
Place a counter at 'Start' on each track.
Toss the coin twice and move the counter on the matching track one space
forward. Continue tossing the coin and moving counters until one counter
reaches 'Finish' to win.
Play several games. Start by predicting which track will win each time.

(123)

Materials
3 counters
A coin

Name _____

Solving problems (I)

Solve these problems.

1. A group of people share **3** cars to go to a party. Each car holds **5** people, including the driver. How many people go to the party?

2. Michael earns some money on Saturday by washing cars. He washes his mum's car and his next-door neighbour's car. They each pay him **£5·50**. How much money does Michael make?

3. The school is having a raffle to raise money to buy a minibus. Raffle tickets cost **50p** for **1** or **£1** for **3**. Emily's dad buys **£4·50** worth of tickets. How many does he buy?

4. David and John both measure how much they have grown in a year. David was **1·26 m** tall last year. He is **1·36 m** tall this year. John was **1·19 m** tall last year and has grown to **1·27 m** this year. Who has grown more in a year?

5. Tai-san goes to bed at **10 p.m.** every day. She has two videos she wants to watch. One is **90** minutes long and one is 110 minutes long. If she starts watching the videos at **6:45 p.m.**, can she watch them both before bedtime?

6. Jamal isn't feeling very well. The doctor tells him to take **450 ml** of medicine each day. He must take the medicine **5** times a day. How much medicine does he take in each dose?

7. Katie and Ellen get some money for Christmas. Auntie Stella gives them **£10** each. Uncle Peter gives them **£7·50** to share. The girls decide to put the money together to buy a video that costs **£15·98**. How much money do they each have left?

Make up your own stories to solve these problems.

8.  £25 − £10·50 − £4·75 =

9. 90 minutes after 12:15

10. 120 metres ÷ 3 =

Name _____

Solving problems (2)

> Solve these problems.

1. Tom has a job washing windows. He
earns **£2·50** for each
house. One day he
washes the windows
for **5** houses. For
lunch he buys a
sandwich which costs
£1·25 and a
drink which
costs **65p**.

How much money does he
have left at the end of the
day?

2. Four children start a running race at
3:30 p.m. Benji finishes at **4:12 p.m.**
Sarah finishes at **4:27 p.m.** Mariah
finishes at **4:19 p.m.** Zach
finishes at **4:13 p.m.** Write the race
times and the
differences in
time. Write the
race order.

3. Renu and Jo go to the fair. They each
have **£10** to spend. First they share a
car on the Dodgems which costs **£3**.
Then they have two
turns each on the
Big Wheel, which
costs **£2** a time.
Next they go on
the Ghost Train
which is **50p**
each. How much
money do they have left?
How many turns can they have on the
Water Chute if it costs **£2·50** each?

4. Ben and Amy are planning a joint
birthday party. They invite **25** friends.
21 people accept the
invitation and
16 of them
want to bring
a friend. On the
day of the party
8 people can't
come because they
have a cold. How
many people are at the party?

> Make up your own
> real-life problem.

> Give it to someone
> else to solve.

Name _____

Solving problems (3)

> Always do the part in brackets first.

> Complete these.

I. $(2 + 8) \times 10 =$ ☐

2. $(5 + 7) \times 3 =$ ☐

3. $(12 - 3) \div 3 =$ ☐

4. $(4 \times 2) + 26 =$ ☐

5. $(8 + 2) \times 22 =$ ☐

6. $(34 - 8) \times 5 =$ ☐

7. $10 \times (16 + 4) =$ ☐

8. $(2 \times 3) + 24 =$ ☐

9. $(32 - 16) \times 2 =$ ☐

10. $(4 + 4) \times 4 =$ ☐

II. $(12 + 8) \times 4 =$ ☐

12. $17 - (2 \times 8) =$ ☐

13. $29 + (3 \times 8) =$ ☐

14. $(16 \div 8) \times 44 =$ ☐

15. $(32 \div 4) - 4 =$ ☐

16. $(10 \times 9) - 9 =$ ☐

17. $(2 + 6) \times (3 + 2) =$ ☐

> Solve these problems.

18. Jada bought **4** boxes of sweets. She ate **6** sweets and had **14** left. How many sweets in each box?

19. Sam had **10** tubes of tennis balls. He lost **8** balls and had **32** left. How many tennis balls were in each tube?

20. Craig has **£20**. He buys **2** lights and a bell for his bike. The bell costs **£7** and he has **£2** left. How much is each light?

21. Amit has bought some new football stickers. He already has some of them, so he gives **8** friends **3** stickers each. He has **6** stickers left. How many stickers did he have to start with? Stickers are sold in packs of **5**. How many packs did he buy?

22. Elspeth cycles to her friend Kim's house. Together they cycle **4** miles to the beach and later they cycle back. Then Elspeth cycles home again. She cycled **15** miles in total. How far is it from Elspeth's house to Kim's house?

To The Beach

126

Name _____

Solving problems (4)

Solve these problems.

---

1. A mystery number is a multiple of **11**. It is also a multiple of **6**. It is less than **200**. It is divisible by **9**. What is the number?

2. A newspaper holds a picture-painting competition for children. The theme is 'Pets'. The newspaper recieves **106** entries. There are **47** pictures of dogs, **29** of cats and **13** of rabbits. How many children painted other kinds of pets?

---

3. Kelly shares a box of **24** sweets with her brother Jamie. She takes **2** sweets for every **1** sweet she gives to Jamie. How many sweets does Jamie get? How many sweets does Kelly get?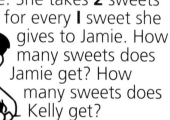

4. A mystery number is a common multiple of **5**, **6**, and **8**. It is greater than **100** and its digit total is **3**. What is the number?

---

5. **35** less **10%** of **50** is $\frac{2}{3}$ of a mystery number. What is the number?

6. The total of three numbers is **10**. One number is a negative number that is a multiple of **5**. One number is a square number. One number is a prime number. All three are 2-digit numbers less than **20**. What are the three numbers?

---

7. Marek is looking at his grandmother's photo album. There are **2** black-and-white photos to every **5** colour photos. If there are **56** photos in the album, how many are colour?

8. When a mystery number is increased by **4·6** then multiplied by **5**, the answer is **27·5**. What is the mystery number?